PINACOTECA

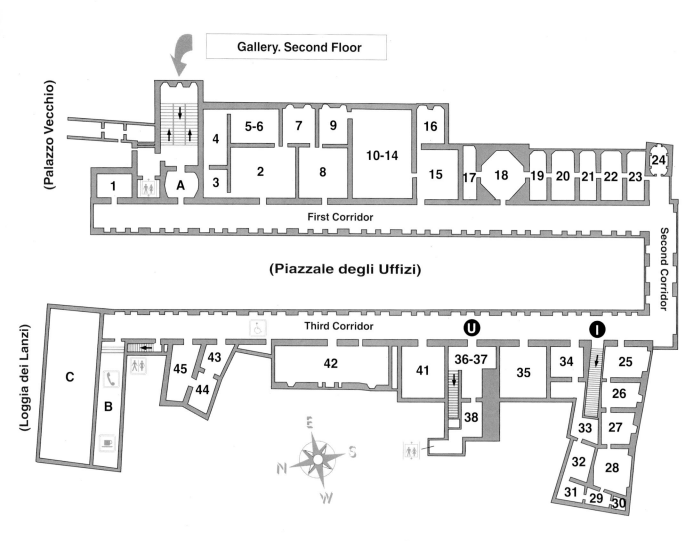

Gallery. Second Floor

(Palazzo Vecchio)

	5-6	7	9	16
4				
	2	8	10-14	15
1	A	3		

17 18 19 20 21 22 23 24

First Corridor

(Piazzale degli Uffizi)

Second Corridor

(Loggia dei Lanzi)

Third Corridor   **U**   **I**

C B

43 45 44 42 41 36-37 35 34 25

38 33 26 27 32 28 31 29 30

N E S W

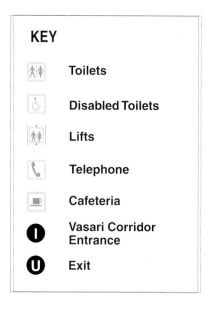

KEY

🚻	Toilets
♿	Disabled Toilets
🛗	Lifts
☎	Telephone
☕	Cafeteria
I	Vasari Corridor Entrance
U	Exit

1 Archaeological Collection
2 Giotto and the 13th century
3 Sienese Painting of the 14th century
4 Florentine Painting of the 14th century
5-6 International Gothic
7 The Early Renaissance
8 Lippi
9 Pollaiolo
10-14 Botticelli
15 Leonardo
16 Geographical Maps
17 Hermaphrodite
18 Tribuna
19 Perugino and Signorelli
20 Dürer
21 Giambellino and Giorgione
22 Flemish and German Renaissance
23 Mantegna and Correggio
24 Cabinet of Miniatures
25 Michelangelo and the Florentine Painting

26 Raphael and Andrea del Sarto
27 Pontormo and Rosso Fiorentino
28 Titian and Sebastiano del Piombo
29 Dosso and Parmigianino
30 Cabinet of Emilian 16th century Painting
31 Veronese
32 Bassano and Tintoretto
33 Corridor of the 16th century
34 Lombard Painting of the 16th century
35 Barocci and the Tuscan Counter-Reformation
36-37 Atrium exit
38 Archaeological Collection
41 Rubens
42 Niobe
43 Painting of the 17th century
44 Flemish Painting of the 17th century
45 Painting of the 18th century
A Lorraine Atrium and ticket check
B Belvedere
C Loggia dei Lanzi Terrace

THE UFFIZI

The official guide
All of the works

Gloria Fossi

GIUNTI

FIRENZE
MVSEI

Texts
Gloria Fossi

Managing editor
Claudio Pescio

Editing
Augusta Tosone

Translation
Catherine Frost, Harriet Paterson, Marina Pugliano

Graphics and page format
Fabio Filippi

Itineraries
Fabio Filippi *and* Stefano Benini

Photographs
Giunti Archive, Stefano Giraldi, Nicola Grifoni
and Rabatti & Domingie Photography – Florence

www.giunti.it

First edition: November 1999
Second revised edition: May 2003
Third revised edition: June 2004

Editorial production by Giunti Editore S.p.A., Florence-Milan

Reprint	Year
5 4 3 2	2007 2006 2005

Printed by Giunti Industrie Grafiche S.p.A. – Prato (Italy)

Contents

Presentation

ENOUGH BOOKS HAVE been written about the public museums in Florence run by the Soprintendenza Speciale per il Polo Museale Fiorentino to fill a large library. This is hardly surprising when one considers that the artistic heritage preserved in our museums has been famous throughout the world for centuries. For hundreds of years writers, scholars and travellers of every nationality and country have been attempting to describe all that the Florentine museums contain. They have made great efforts to explain why these museums are so fascinating, and to lead a path through paintings and sculptures for both the uninformed but willing visitor and the refined and jaded intellectual.

Over time, however, the museums have altered their aspect and their layout, the exhibitions have been arranged in new ways, the collections have been enriched (or impoverished). Attributions of works in the museums have also changed, restorations have transformed the appearance of many pieces, the rise and fall of aesthetic tendencies have led to reorganization and the exhibition of differing works. All these things are constantly taking place within the public collections because museology and the history of art, like any intellectual endeavour, are in a constant state of progress and transformation. This explains why the literature surrounding the Florentine museums (like that of any of the world's great art collections) is so immense, and in a process of continual updating and change.

The perfect, definitive guide to a museum, any museum, does not and cannot exist.

The premise seems obvious, but is nonetheless necessary in order to understand the point of the publication introduced by these lines. From the moment when, in accordance with the application of the Ronchey Law 4/93, the Giunti publishing house group took over the running of the support services within the Florentine museum system, it was decided to start at once on a standardised series of illustrated guides. These guides, displaying the cuneiform flower of Firenze Musei on the cover, guarantee that at the year of publication the state of each museum is exactly that described in the guide.

Certain things are obviously necessary if a museum guide is to aspire to reliability, official standing and at the same time enjoy a wide distribution: accuracy of information, high quality reproductions and – not least – a clearly written text (without, naturally, being banal or lacking in precision). Readers will judge for themselves if the guide which follows this introduction reaches these standards. I have no doubt that this will be a serious and committed judgement, just as myself and the Publisher of this guide have been serious and committed in attempting to meet the cultural needs of whoever visits our museums in the best way and with every possible care.

The Superintendent
for Polo Museale Fiorentino
Antonio Paolucci   7

Introduction

ONE OF THE WORLD's most important museums, the Uffizi Gallery was one of the first in Europe to emerge in accordance with the modern idea of a museum, that is to say as a systematically organised exhibition space designed for public viewing. Two centuries before it was officially opened in 1765, the Gallery was in fact open to visitors on request, albeit to a restricted number of "connoisseurs": in 1591 a guide to Florence written by Francesco Bocchi describes it as "amongst the most supremely beautiful sights... in the World... filled with ancient statues, with noble paintings and extremely precious objects". It is worth remembering that it was created in a city which had long since been the first to revisit the disused term museum, which for the ancient Greeks signified a space dedicated to the Muses: in Florence it was used to describe the collection of antique sculptures which Lorenzo the Magnificent (1449-1492) established in the garden at San Marco. Artists such as Leonardo and Michelangelo gathered here "for beauty, for work and for recreation", as Giorgio Vasari relates. This latter was not only the architect of the Uffizi but also the author of the Lives of the Artists published in 1550 and in 1568, a work which will frequently be referred to in this guide.

The origins of the Uffizi date back to 1560, when at the request of the Medici duke Cosimo I (1519-1574), Vasari designed a grand palazzo with two wings, "along the river, almost floating in the air", which housed the Magistrature, or the administrative and judicial offices – Uffizi – of the duchy of Tuscany. Five years later Vasari oversaw in a few short months the building of the elevated gallery which, connecting the Uffizi to the new Medici residence at Palazzo Pitti, runs to this day over the Ponte Vecchio and the church of Santa Felicita, leading out into the Boboli gardens. In a unique urban relationship, the Vasari Corridor unites the nerve centres of city: the river, the oldest bridge and the seats of power, along a spectacular elevated walkway, used at the time exclusively by the court. But it is to Cosimo's son, Francesco I (1541-1587), that we owe the first real nucleus of the Gallery. The introverted Grand Duke had already established a Studiolo filled with paintings and precious objects in his residence in the Palazzo Vecchio, which was later also joined to the Uffizi by an elevated passageway. Around 1581 he transformed the top floor of the Uffizi into a gallery, a place for "walking, with paintings, statues and other precious things", and in 1586 gave the eclectic Bernardo Buontalenti the task of creating the Medici Theatre. This provided a space for memorable performances, and corresponded in height to the present first and second floors of the museum in the eastern wing of the building where we now find the collections of graphic works and other exhibition rooms.

The Gallery was illuminated by large windows, decorated by antique sculptures and by frescoes on the ceiling. But the most creative idea was the Tribune: a symbolic, unusual, welcoming space, its octagonal cupola encrusted with shells, filled with works of art and furnishings, all lit from above. Near the Tribune is a terrace which was closed in by the Grand Duke Ferdinando, brother of Francesco, in 1589, to create the Loggia of Geographical Maps (Room 16). At the end of the other wing, the western one, a hanging garden was created over Orcagna's Loggia, beyond the Foundry and other workshops. Nowadays the Uffizi Gallery boasts an incomparable artistic heritage: thousands of pictures from the medieval to the modern age, ancient sculptures, miniatures, tapestries; it holds an unrivalled position for its series of self-portraits which is constantly growing through acquisitions and through donations by contemporary artists, equalled only by its collection in the Cabinet of Drawings and Prints, outstanding even for this city which traditionally prides itself on being "preeminent in drawing". If the Uffizi Gallery can rightly be called a museum par excellence, this is not just because of its superb buildings and its works of art. Its unique quality also comes from the origins of its collections, from its history which goes back more than four centuries and which is so closely entwined with the events of Florentine civilisation. That the Uffizi is a byword for Florence and vice-versa is explained above all by the inborn vocation for collecting of its governors, with the Medici leading the way: the lords of Florence for three centuries, they were also passionate patrons and collectors of antiquities from the time of Cosimo the Elder (1389-1464) who was the patron of artists such as the transgressive Fra Filippo Lippi (Room 8).

b

The first Medicean collections form, as mentioned earlier, the original nucleus of the Gallery. How-ever it is also true, as the reader of this guide will realise from the provenances of the works cata-logued here, that many works of art destined for other locations which eventually found their way to this great U-shaped building in the heart of the city reflect the tastes and choices of both public figures and private citizens, of merchants, bankers and literati as well as of civic and religious institutions. One need only mention, in connection with the early fifteenth century, the cultured and vastly wealthy Palla Strozzi, who approached Gentile da Fabriano, a stranger in Florence, for an Adoration of the Magi *for his chapel in Santa Trinita: a work which in its exotic magic is a long way from the simple, essential world being evoked in those years by the Tuscan artist Masaccio.*

This latter worked with Masolino for the powerful Felice Brancacci, and before that for the religious sisters of Sant'Ambrogio (Room 7).

For the sixteenth century one should at least mention Agnolo Doni, patron of Michelangelo (Room 25) and also of Raphael, as well as Lorenzo Nasi who commissioned of the artist from Urbino the Madonna of the Goldfinch *(Room 26); and Bartolomeo Panciatichi, painted together with his ex-tremely beautiful wife by Bronzino (Tribune). The Florentine guilds were also important patrons dur-ing the fourteenth and fifteenth centuries; amongst these were the Bankers Guild, who commissioned a triptych from Orcagna for the pillar on its property in Orsanmichele, the seat of the Arts (Room 4), and the Merchants' Guild, who asked Piero Pollaiolo and then Botticelli for a series of* Virtues *for its Tribunal (Room 9). Lastly, many works now in the Gallery exist thanks to the patronage of the churches, confraternities and monasteries in and around Florence, from which, furthermore, various artist-monks emerged such as Fra Angelico, Lorenzo Monaco and Fra Bartolomeo (Rooms 5-6, 7, 25). There are other historical considerations which add to the unique nature of the Uffizi's collections:*

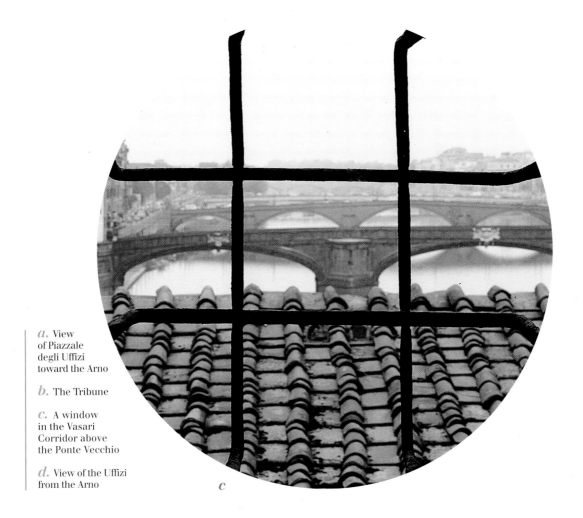

a. View
of Piazzale
degli Uffizi
toward the Arno

b. The Tribune

c. A window
in the Vasari
Corridor above
the Ponte Vecchio

d. View of the Uffizi
from the Arno

c

since the fourteenth century Florence has had a closely-woven international network which has led, often through indirect routes, to fruitful exchange with foreign artistic influences: the Portinari, agents of the Medici in Bruges, sent the imposing Van der Goes Triptych to the church of Sant'Egidio (Room 10-14), and had themselves painted by the Flemish Memling (Room 22). In addition, official visits by dignitaries and high-ranking prelates almost always brought some artistic novelty or other to the banks of the Arno: a chapel in San Miniato was dedicated to the Cardinal of Portugal who died in Florence in 1459, and it was from this chapel that the magnificent Altarpiece of Pollaiolo (Room 9) came. For the marriage of Maria de' Medici to Henri IV (1600), the Vicenzan Filippo Pigafetta (1533-1604) published a description of the Gallery for strangers to the city and planned a room of military architecture (Room 17). Diplomatic gifts, dowries and inheritances from international marriages enlarged the collections of the grand dukes, who were developing more and more of a taste for works from other Italian and foreign schools and contemporary, non-Florentine artists. A few examples: Ferdinando I (1549-1609), who had already acquired in Rome in 1583 the famous and only recently discovered antique sculptural group of the Wrestlers (in the Tribune since 1677), received as a gift from Cardinal del Monte the Medusa by Caravaggio and inherited miniatures and other works from his wife Christine of Lorraine, grand-daughter of Caterina de' Medici. Ferdinand II (1610-1670) inherited through his wife Vittoria della Rovere the Piero della Francesca Diptych (Room 7) and Titian's Venus of Urbino (Room 28), amongst other things, and acquired Nordic paintings through the artist Agostino Tassi, the Medici's first artistic intermediary. Cosimo II (1590-1621) was an admirer of the Emilian Guercino as was his son, the erudite Cardinal Leopoldo (1617-1675), who founded the Accademia del Cimento, and formed the first collections of self-portraits and drawings. Cosimo III (1642-1723) bought foreign paintings, particularly Flemish ones, such as the two great canvases of

d

Rubens damaged by the 1993 bomb, now restored. And finally the Grand Prince Ferdinand (1663-1713) invited artists like Giuseppe Maria Crespi, Magnasco and the two Riccis to Florence. When the Medici dynasty died out, the last heir Anna Maria Luisa (1667-1743) sanctioned the Gallery as "public and inalienable property", granting the Uffizi a new lease of life during the Grand Duchy of Lorraine, especially under the enlightened figure of Pietro Leopoldo (Grand Duke of Tuscany from 1765 to 1790), to whom we owe the entrance stairways, the vestibule and the Niobe Room. A renewed taste for primitives led to the acquisition of earlier works, which often came from suppressed convents and monasteries; the nucleus of French painting was formed at that time and the first "scientific" guides were published (Bencivenni Pelli, 1779; Luigi Lanzi, 1782).

From the nineteenth century onwards, the growth of the picture gallery has brought about new displays and new rooms, a process which, despite changing circumstances, has been almost uninterrupted to this day, notwithstanding the bomb of 1993. During the postwar period, various rearrangements and restorations have been carried out by Roberto Salvini, Luisa Becherucci and Luciano Berti. Many other high-profile interventions have taken place since 1987 under the current director Annamaria Petrioli Tofani, who, with the conservators Giovanni Agosti, Caterina Caneva, Alessandro Cecchi, Antonio Natali, Piera Bocci Pacini and the architect Antonio Godoli, has carried out the restoration of the Royal Postroom on the ground floor; of various exhibition rooms on the first floor; the philological restoration of the Gallery's three corridors and the reorganisation following new criteria of many of the rooms (8 and 15 in the eastern wing and most of the rooms in the west wing). Since 1998 work has been proceeding to extend the museum into the vast areas beneath the Gallery, according to a detailed reconstruction plan in which the Environmental and Architectural Heritage Service is also involved.

Owing to an improved layout of tapestries, paintings and other works from the museum's deposits – with consequent changes and altered positions for works already on display, particularly for the seventeenth and eighteenth century paintings which until now were cramped in the last room of the Third corridor – it will be possible to trace an ever-more meaningful art-history journey through schools and eras. Already in operation on the ground floor are the new welcoming and service facilities (public entrance, ticket office, bookshop, information), housed in the rooms which were once the headquarters of the ancient Florentine Magistrature.

The remarkable Contini Bonacossi collection, previously in the Meridiana pavilion at Palazzo Pitti, has also finally been given a definitive display. There is a temporary entrance from Via Lambertesca but the collection will soon be linked directly to the rest of the museum. In addition, on the first floor, the spectacular Loggia on the Arno (corresponding to the Gallery's Southern Corridor), which was inaugurated in December 1998 after restoration (originally open, it is now enclosed by windows which offer a magnificent panorama over the city) is an integral part of the New Uffizi. Within the general context of renovation, the priceless collection of over sixty thousand volumes in the Uffizi's Library of Art History has been rearranged in the vast, well-lit area of the old Baldracca Theatre, rebuilt between 1716 and 1727 to house the Library Magliabechiana (its thirty thousand volumes bequeathed in 1714 by the erudite Giovanni Magliabechi now form the original core of the Florence National Central Library). This spectacular 18th century hall, now equipped with functional reading and lighting systems, is reached by the monumental Magliabechian stairway, on the ground floor of the Uffizi's eastern loggia.

Lastly, a new exit from the Uffizi is now being built, according to the design of the Japanese architect Arata Isozaki, winner of a competition held in the Spring of 1999 among architects of world-wide fame. Visitors to the Uffizi now exit on Piazza Castellani, on the eastern side of the museum complex.

Gloria Fossi

Note

Obviously, the appearance of a museum, especially one as vast and important as the Uffizi Gallery, changes continually. And this is also its fascination. Accordingly, if the reader does not always find on display, on the very day of his visit, everything he is looking for, all in its proper place, we must ask him to be patient. No matter what efforts the author has made, with the collaboration of all those who work with commitment in the museum every day, and whom we wish to thank, it is impossible to "photograph" today the overall situation in the certainty that all of the works on display will remain in their places exactly as we have seen and described them. In our case this is due not only to the usual transferrals for restoration, temporary loan for exhibitions, and the changing locations of works retrieved from the storage deposits. The Uffizi Gallery has for some time been engaged in large-scale extension and reorganization, which may involve the temporary closing of some rooms and the repositioning of certain works not predictable at present, as well as substantial rearrangement of entire rooms, especially on the Gallery's First Floor, opened to the public in March 2004. After the reopening in 1998 of the Niobe Room and in 1999 of Room 35 dedicated to Barocci and the artists of the Tuscan Counter-reformation, in April 2001 the Rooms at the end of the Third Corridor containing a selection from the very rich collections of 17th and 18th century paintings were reopened. For this section, pending definitive arrangement within the context of the New Uffizi project, we have listed all of the works on display with descriptions of some of the most important paintings. As regards the collection of sculptures, only the ancient statues in the three corridors (busts excluded) are listed here, with updating on restoration. For more detailed information, see our volume *Uffizi Gallery. Art, History, Collections* (Florence 2002²) and the guidebook by Fabrizio Paolucci and Giovanni Di Pasquale, *The Ancient Sculptures in the Uffizi* (Florence 2001). Lastly, Room 1-Archeological Collections is scheduled to reopen soon in the First Corridor.

How to read the catalogued lists

This guide contains a complete catalogue of all of the works exhibited in the Gallery, room by room. For each room (except Room 35 and Rooms 41-45) there is a plan showing the arrangement of the works of art. The encircled numbers refer to the lists in which all of the works are catalogued. The small images appearing beside some numbers, in the border around the floor plan, indicate that a commentary on these works is given on the following pages. In the lists measurements are given in centimetres unless otherwise indicated. As regards the authors of some paintings whose identification is still subject to research that is constantly evolving thanks also to the new restorations noted here, the most convincing attributions have been indicated, at times accompanied by the traditional ones (bibliographical references appear at the end of the guide). As regards dating, often equally controversial, the discordant hypotheses of various experts have at times been reported, regardless of our own personal opinions (for example, in some famous works by Paolo Uccello, Leonardo and Caravaggio).

The Hall of San Pier Scheraggio

Erected over the foundation of a 9th century religious building and consecrated in 1068, the church of San Pier Scheraggio was until 1313 the seat of the town councils and the site of memorable public speeches by Dante and Boccaccio. Some of the arches of the left nave, which was destroyed in 1410 to enlarge Via della Ninna, are still visible from the exterior. Among the remaining Medieval structures, incorporated into the ground floor of the Uffizi in 1560, the central nave still stands, which since 1971 has been restored but is not open to the public at present. Of note amongst the works on display here, which include decorative fragments from the Roman and Medieval ages, is the so-called Madonna of Childbirth, *here since its origins, formerly attributed to the Master of San Martino alla Palma and probably conceived in Bernardo Daddi's workshop, and a* Madonna *by the Master of Greve, an emblematic example of the sensational restoration which in 1986 brought to light figures that had been entirely painted over. The room is now dominated by Andrea del Castagno's cycle of humanistic frescoes, recovered in 1847 from Villa Carducci, and in the Uffizi since 1969. In the humanistic environment of the 15th century the artist emphesised the social status of characters from recent Florentine history by depicting them together with heroic figures from the Bible and antiquity. The monumental* Battle *painted by Cagli in 1936 for the Milan Triennal, donated to the Uffizi in 1983, is also here, although only temporarily.*

The works

1. ANDREA DEL CASTAGNO
Queen Esther
c. 1449-1450
Detached fresco
transferred to canvas
120x150
San Marco and Cenacoli Inv. no. 169

2. ANDREA DEL CASTAGNO
The Cumaean Sibyl
c. 1449-1450
Detached fresco
transferred to canvas
250x154
San Marco and Cenacoli Inv. no. 170

3. ANDREA DEL CASTAGNO
Queen Tomyris
c. 1449-1450
Detached fresco
transferred to canvas
254x155
San Marco and Cenacoli Inv. no. 168

4. ANDREA DEL CASTAGNO
Giovanni Boccaccio
c. 1449-1450
Detached fresco
transferred to canvas
250x154
San Marco and Cenacoli Inv. no. 165

5. ANDREA DEL CASTAGNO
Francesco Petrarca
c. 1449-1450
Detached fresco transferred to canvas
257x153
San Marco and Cenacoli Inv. no. 166

6. ANDREA DEL CASTAGNO
Dante Alighieri
c. 1449-1450
Detached fresco transferred to canvas
247x153
San Marco and Cenacoli Inv. no. 167

7. MASTER OF GREVE
Madonna with Child and Annunciation
Mid-13th century
Tempera on wood
180x78
Inv. 1890 no. 9494
Restored: 1986

8. ANDREA DEL CASTAGNO
Niccolò Acciaioli
c. 1449-1450
Detached fresco
transferred to canvas
250x154
San Marco and Cenacoli Inv. no. 171

9. ANDREA DEL CASTAGNO
Pippo Spano
c. 1449-1450
Detached fresco
transferred to canvas
250x154
San Marco and Cenacoli Inv. no. 173

10. ANDREA DEL CASTAGNO
Farinata degli Uberti
c. 1449-1450
Detached fresco
transferred to canvas
250x154
San Marco and Cenacoli Inv. no. 172

11. MASTER OF SAN MARTINO ALLA PALMA (OR WORKSHOP OF BERNARDO DADDI)
Madonna crowned by two Angels, known as "Madonna of Childbirth" or "Ninna"
c. 1340
Tempera on wood
230x117
Inv. 1890 no. 6165

12. CORRADO CAGLI
Battle of San Martino
1936
Encaustic tempera
on plywood
545x651
Without Inv. no.

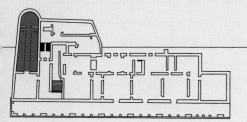

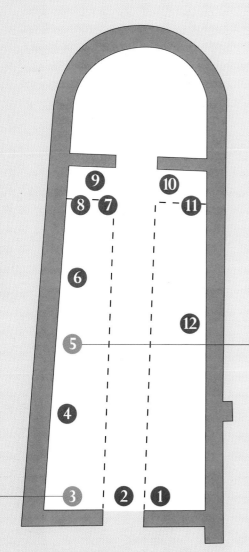

5

ANDREA DEL CASTAGNO
Francesco Petrarca

In the cycle of famous Florentines at Villa Carducci, the portrait of Petrarca with those of Dante and Boccaccio represents the virtues of literature. Among the other personages are the Ghibelline Farinata degli Uberti and the banker Niccolò Acciaioli, who died at Naples in 1365.

DOMINVS FRANCISCHVS PETRARCHA

3

ANDREA DEL CASTAGNO
Queen Tomyris

In his *Memoriale* of 1510, Francesco Albertini records that Andrea del Castagno painted a "most beautiful" loggia, with "Sibyls and famous Florentine men", for Gonfalonier Carducci's home in Legnaia, on the outskirts of Florence. The cycle's decorative fragments include the Cumaean Sibyl, the ancient heroines Queens Esther and Tomyris, and six famous Florentines.

The figures are almost sculptural in form – standing out against feigned panels they create an effect of three–dimensional space around them.

Cabinet of Prints and Drawings

The traditional gift of Florentine artists for drawing dates back to at least the time of Cennino Cennini, a painter as well as the author of a treatise on artistic techniques, who at in the beginning of the 15ᵗʰ century considered drawing "the foundation of art". A further significant claim was then made in the 16ᵗʰ century by the great draftsman Pontormo, who considered drawing to be the noblest form of expression. One of the first people to value drawing as a separate art was Giorgio Vasari, fervent collector, capable draftsman, and an expert on technique. Since the time of Lorenzo the Medici had also collected drawings, but it was under Cardinal Leopoldo (1617-1675) that the true beginnings of the Uffizi collection, then in the Pitti, were laid down. Today this is the most outstanding collection of graphic works in Italy, and one of the most important in the world: it boasts works of fundamental importance from the 14ᵗʰ-15ᵗʰ centuries to the present day, and contains works by great masters such as Leonardo, Michelangelo, Raphael, Andrea del Sarto, Pontormo and many others. The rooms it currently occupies while waiting for future enlargements are on the first floor, in areas created from the 16ᵗʰ century Medici Theatre. The works are only on view for the purposes of study, but themed exhibitions, usually held in the long hall shown on the layout, are periodically open to the public.

RAPHAEL
Nude Study
c. 1509
Charcoal and white chalk
on yellowed white paper
mm 357x210
Inv. G.D.S.U. no. 541 E r.

This was the preparatory drawing for the figure of Adam in the fresco of the *Disputation over the Sacrament* in Raphael's Stanza della Segnatura (1509) in the Vatican. Outstanding draftsman, the vigorous lines with which he sketches this almost sculptural nude show that he had studied the work of Michelangelo as well as antique sculpture; it comes as little surprise that in 1515 Raphael was named Head of Roman Antiquities by the Medici Pope, Leo X.

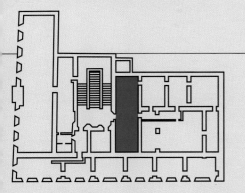

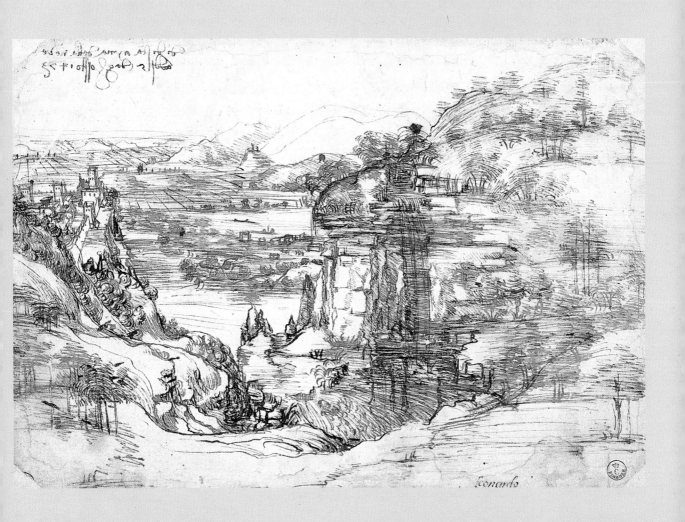

LEONARDO DA VINCI
Landscape
Dated on the top left corner:
"dì di Santa Maria della neve
addì 5 d'aghossto 1473"
Pen on yellowed white paper
mm 196x287
G.D.S.U. Inv. no. 8 P r.
From the Fondo Mediceo Lorenese

This is the first known dated work of Leonardo's and the first drawing of pure landscape in western art. It dates back, as indicated by Leonardo's mirror writing, to the day of the miraculous summer snowfall on the Esquiline Hill in Rome. Possibly showing the Arno valley as viewed from the mountainside of Montalbano, the drawing witnesses to Leonardo's interest in nature.

First Corridor

After a restoration in 1996, the East Corridor has largely recovered its late 16th century appearance, conceived by Francesco I, founder of the Gallery. The restoration of the corridor and its display of statues and paintings is based upon the drawings of the Gallery carried out by Fra Benedetto Vincenzo de Greyss and assistants between 1748 and 1765. Following the categories defined in 1597 by Filippo Pigafetta, the older portraits from the Giovio Series, partly restored, have been placed under the ceiling, which is decorated with grotesque motifs. The series depicts famous men from every age and country, and was begun for Cosimo I by Cristofano dell'Altissimo, who in Como (1552-1589) copied the renowned collection by Paolo Giovio. The paintings passed from Palazzo Vecchio to the Pitti Palace, and then to the Uffizi in 1587. After more than two centuries, the portraits of the Aulic Series are now set back in regular spaces beneath the Giovio Series. Francesco I and his successors commissioned these to extol their family, beginning with the founder, Giovanni di Bicci. They were inspired by older prototypes, some of which are still in the Tribune. Ancient busts and sculptures from the Medici collection alternate along the walls. The ceilings with grotesque decoration were executed by a group of painters led by Alessandro Allori (Antonio Tempesta, Ludovico Buti, Giovan Maria Butteri and Ludovico Cigoli). The pavement in large white and grey marble squares dates back to the Lorraine period (18th century).

The statues

1. *Hercules and Nessus the Centaur*
Fragment of Roman copy
of an original from century 300 BC,
restored in the 16th century
Greek marble
Inv. 1914 no. 77

2. *Funerary relief with busts
of husband and wife*
1st century AD
Italic marble
Inv. 1914 no. 78

3. *Seated woman with portrait head*
Roman copy of an original
from the late 5th century BC
Pentelic marble
Inv. 1914 no. 171

4. *Seated woman*
Roman copy, Imperial Age,
of an Attic original, 430-420 BC
Greek marble
Inv. 1914 no. 196

5. *Demeter*
Roman copy of an Attic original,
430-400 BC
Black and Parian marble
Inv. 1914 no. 276

6. *Apollo known as "from Omphalòs"*
Roman copy, from the time
of Antonius, of an Greek
original bronze, 470-460 BC
Pentelic marble
(ancient head, not pertinent,
in Parian marble)
Inv. 1914 no. 175
Restored: 1995

7. *Funerary statue of a youth known
as Marcus Aurelius*
Roman copy from the 1st century AD
Greek marble
Inv. 1914 no. 258

8. *Leda*
Roman copy, 2nd century AD,
of a 4th century Greek original,
perhaps by Skopas
Head not pertinent
Pentelic and Parian marble
Inv. 1914 no. 239

9. *Nymph with panther*
Roman copy,
Imperial Age,
of an original
from the late 2nd century BC
Parian marble
Inv. 1914 no. 274
Restored: 1995

10. *Athlete known as
"Apoxyomenos"*
Copy, 1st century AD,
of a Greek original
from the 4th century BC
Greek marble
Inv. 1914 no. 100

11. *Young satyr, known as "Mercury"*
Roman copy of an original
of Praxitelean influence
Parian marble
Inv. 1914 no. 250
Restored: 1995

12. *Woman sacrificing,
previously known as
"Vestal"*
From the time of Severus
Greek marble
Inv. 1914 no. 131

13. *Horus*
Roman copy,
second half of the 1st century AD,
of a Greek original
from the early 4th century BC
Luni marble
Inv. 1914 no. 136

14. *Satyr*
Roman copy, 2nd-3rd century AD,
of a Greek original bronze from
the second half of the 2nd century BC
Pentelic marble
Inv. 1914 no. 108

15. *Discus-thrower*
Roman copy from the torso
of Myron's *Discus-thrower* (c. 450 BC)
The head, not pertinent, is a copy
of an *Alexander the Great*
of the "Barracco" type
(3rd century BC)
Parian marble
Inv. 1914 no. 212
Restored: 1994

16. *Figure of a woman,
previous known as "Ariadne"*
Roman copy
of a Greek original bronze
from the Hellenistic age
Pentelic marble
Inv. 1914 no. 122

17. *Venus and Cupid*
Roman copy, from the time
of Antonius, of a late
Hellenistic original, 150-120 BC
Greek and Apuan marble
Inv. 1914 no. 153

18. *Lance-bearer*
Roman copy
from the time of Claudius
of an original of Polyclitean
influence, mid-5th century BC
Pentelic marble
Inv. 1914 no. 114

19. *Seated Apollo (?)*
Roman copy of an original
from the 2nd century BC
Parian marble
Inv. 1914 no. 222

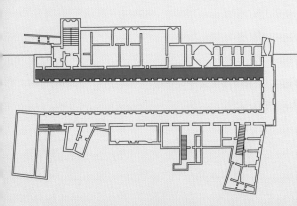

20. *Mars, replica of the*
"Ares Borghese" type
Copy from the time of Nero
of an Attic original from the
first half of the 5ᵗʰ century BC
Black marble
Inv. 1914 no. 192

21. *Venus*
Roman copy, Imperial age,
of an original from the second
half of the 2ⁿᵈ century BC.
Pentelic marble
Inv. 1914 no. 155

22. *Athlete*
Copy from the time of Hadrian of a
Greek original of Polyclitean influence
Pentelic marble
Inv. 1914 no. 107

23. *Bacchus and a Satyr*
16ᵗʰ century Florentine sculptor
working on an ancient torso
from Roman times
Apuan marble and Pentelic marble
Inv. 1914 no. 241

24. *Aesculapius, replica*
of the "Giustini" type
Copy, from the time
of Flavius, of a Greek
original bronze from
the late 4ᵗʰ century BC
Greek marble
Inv. 1914 no. 247

25. *Bacchus and a Satyr*
Roman copy
from the time of Hadrian
Pentelic marble
Inv. 1914 no. 246

26. *Venus and Mars*
Roman copy,
from the time
of Hadrian-Antonius,
of originals from
the 5ᵗʰ-4ᵗʰ century BC
Greek marble
Inv. 1914 no. 4

ALESSANDRO ALLORI
Grotesque decorations
with Medicean devices
1581
Fresco with tempera retouches
345x585

The grotesque, a typical decoration inspired by the friezes in Imperial Roman residences, takes its name from the so-called "grottoes" in Nero's *Domus Aurea* in Rome. Whilst by the end of the fifteenth century grotesque decorations began to appear in the paintings of artists such as Filippino Lippi, Pinturicchio and Signorelli, they were most fully developed in the second half of the sixteenth century, no acci-

dent considering how well the style adapted to the bizarre late-Mannerist taste of the age of Francesco I.

Amongst the subjects of the First Corridor are landscapes, real and fabulous animals, monsters, masks and satyrs, weapons and Medicean devices. In the frescoes of the vault illustrated here, situated half way down the First Corridor, we find various emblems of Francesco I de' Medici (the weasel with a branch of rue and the motto AMAT VICTORIA CURAM, "Victory loves care") and of Bianca Cappello, his lover and later his second wife (the oyster opening in the sun and the motto MAR[I] CŒLOQUE PROCREATA MERITO CARISSIMA, "Deservedly precious, she came forth from the sky and the sea").

FRA BENEDETTO VINCENZO DE GREYSS AND ASSISTANCE

End wall of the First Corridor
1748-1765
Pen on paper
Cabinet of Prints and Drawings, De Greyss
Album (Inv. G.D.S.U. nos. 4569F-4578F, 4579F-4588bis, 4492F-4534F; 4535F-4568F)

In 1748 Francesco Stefano di Lorena commissioned the Dominican monk De Greyss to make an illustrated inventory of the Gallery. Assisted by a team of draftsmen, De Greyss did not complete the set of illustrations, accomplished through the "tocco in penna" technique, which were then to be transposed to printing. On the basis of the remaining folios (now in Florence and Vienna) it has been possible to rearrange some rooms in the Gallery which remained practically unchanged from the 16th century to about 1780. The drawing shown here documents the works displayed at the end of the First Corridor facing Palazzo Vecchio, now rearranged in similar manner. Along the walls, are portraits from the Giovian Series portraying famous condottieri of ancient times. Placed at the centre is *Giovanni di Averardo de' Medici know as di Bicci* (1360-1429), founder of the Medici family, painted by Alessandro Allori in 1585 for the Aulic Series (Inv. no. 2232). Below are three ancient statues from the Medicean collection: *Hercules and Nessus the Centaur* (Inv. no. 77) and two *Seated Women* (Inv. nos. 171, 196).

Room 2 ✦ Giotto and the 13th century

The present arrangement of Room 2 was carried out during the Fifties (architects Gardella, Michelucci and Scarpa, director Salvini). The wide opening in the entering wall allowed for the entry of large-scale works (Cimabue's Crucifixion was previously hung here, and later returned to Santa Croce where it was damaged by the 1966 flood). Alongside some precious examples of very early Tuscan painting (some of the painters, for the most part from Pisa, Lucca and Florence, are still unknown), this first room with its truss-framed ceiling reminiscent of a Medieval church houses three imposing Maestas by Cimabue, Duccio and Giotto. Their recent restorations have provided new, important readings and confirm the great skill of Florentine carpenters in carrying out the complex carpentry of these three huge panels.

The works

1. FLORENTINE SCHOOL
Madonna and Child
c. 1250
Tempera on wood
98x60
Inv. 1890 no. 9213

**2. FLORENTINE MASTER
(ATTR. MASTER OF THE BARDI
ST. FRANCIS)**
*Crucifix with eight stories
of the Passion*
c. 1240
Tempera on wood
250x200
Inv. 1890 no. 434

3. MASTER OF MADDALENA
St. Luke the Evangelist
Second half
of the 13th century
Tempera on wood
132x50
Inv. 1890 no. 3493

4. DUCCIO DI BONINSEGNA
Maestà (The Rucellai Madonna)
c. 1285
Tempera on wood
450x293
Without Inv. no.
Restored: 1989

5. GIOTTO
Badia Polyptych
c. 1300
Tempera on wood
91x334
Dep. S. Croce Inv. no. 7

6. GIOTTO
Maestà (The Ognissanti Madonna)
c. 1310
Tempera on wood
325x204
Inv. 1890 no. 8344
Restored: 1991

7. MASTER OF SAN TORPÈ
Madonna and Child
Early 14th century
Tempera on wood
60x38.3
Inv. 1890 no. 9920

8. CIMABUE
Maestà of Santa Trinita
Datable between 1280 and 1290
Tempera on wood
425x243
Inv. 1890 no. 8343
Restored: 1993

9. PISAN SCHOOL
Crucifix with stories of the Passion
Last quarter of the 12th century
Tempera on wood
377x231
Inv. 1890 no. 432

10. MELIORE
*The Redeemer with the Virgin
and Sts. Peter, John and Paul*

Signed and dated 1271
Tempera on wood
85x210
Inv. 1890 no. 9153

**11. FOLLOWER OF BONAVENTURA
BERLINGHIERI (ATTR. MASTER
OF THE OBLATE CRUCIFIXION)**
Madonna and Child
and *Crucifixion*
c. 1250
Tempera on wood
103x122 (entire diptych)
Inv. 1890 nos. 8575-8576

**12. SCHOOL OF BONAVENTURA
BERLINGHIERI
(ALSO ATTR. MASTER
OF THE BARDI ST. FRANCIS)**
The stigmata of St. Francis
c. 1250
Tempera on wood
81x51
Inv. 1890 no. 8574

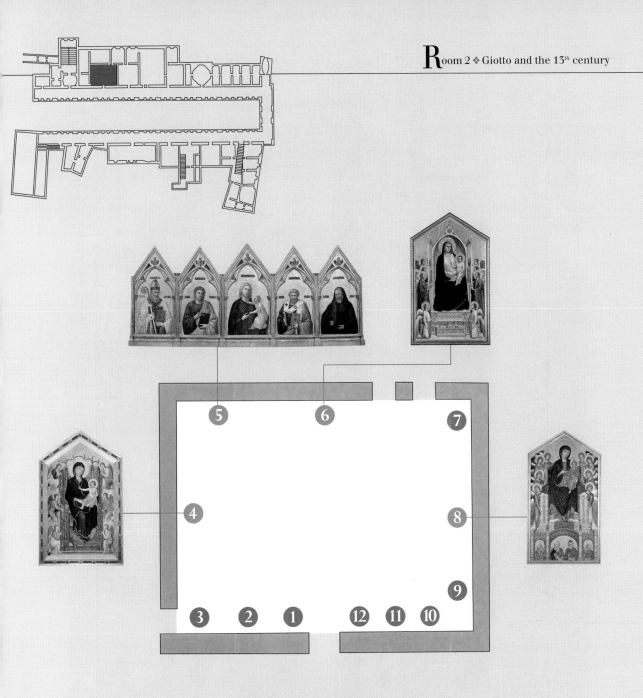

4

DUCCIO DI BONINSEGNA
Maestà (The Rucellai Madonna)

Painted by Duccio for the Laudesi Confraternity Chapel in Santa Maria Novella, this is the first known large work of the Sienese painter. The outstanding frame, integrated into the altarpiece, surrounds the Madonna enthroned between six kneeling angels with thirty medallions showing saints and half-length Biblical figures, portrayed with intensity despite the small dimensions.

5

GIOTTO
Badia Polyptych

Formerly on the main altar of the Badia Fiorentina, this panel painting shows the Madonna with Child, flanked on the left by St. John the Evangelist and St. Nicholas and on the right by St. Peter and St. Benedict. On each pinnacle stands a small tondo (God the Father in the middle and angels on each side). Because of its articulated, architectural structure with pointed divisions and trefoiled frames from which the saints appear to lean out, and for its sensitive use of chiaroscuro and its fine detail, the polyptych is considered to be the work of Giotto, completed after his travels to Rome and Rimini, and before his stay in Padua.

25

6

GIOTTO
Maestà (The Ognissanti Madonna)

Painted for the Umiliati Altar, as recently proven, to the right side of the door of the screen wall in the church of Ognissanti, the gaze of the Madonna and the position of the throne in fact suggest it should be viewed from the right side, as with Duccio's *Maestà* in Santa Maria Novella.

This large, devotional work is a homage to the virginity, maternity, and royalty of Mary.

An angel offers her a precious crown, while another is giving the Child the eucharistic pyx, representing the Passion of Christ. Two angels at the Virgin's feet offer an ampulla with roses and lilies, both Marian symbols.

Note the extraordinary perspective effect, with the figures solidly arranged in a space rendered lifelike by the three-dimensional throne. Note also the realism of the faces, of the variegated marble, of the flowers painted from nature and even of the wood of the platform at the feet of the Madonna.

8

CIMABUE
Maestà of Santa Trinita

This large panel painting, whose original frame is lost, was meant to stand 465 cm high on the main altar of the church of Santa Trinita, striking the view of all the faithful at once. Eight foreshortened angels flank the Madonna with Child. Below, between the arches, Jeremiah and Isaiah look upwards to confirm the prophecies inscribed on the scrolls, concerning the virginal birth of Jesus; in the middle are Abraham and David, from whose offspring the Saviour would rise.

Room 3 ❖ Sienese Painting of the 14ᵗʰ century

A refined, otherworldly art, embellished by gold-leaf, multicolored fabrics, elaborate floor-ing and marble overlay awaits the visitor to this small room, restored in the Fifties like the one before it. It is dedicated to the supreme moment of Sienese painting, the 14ᵗʰ century, a time when this Tuscan city, close to Florence but far removed from it in many aspects of its figura-tive culture, expressed to the highest degree an artistic sensitivity represented primarily by Si-mone Martini with his brother-in-law Lippo Memmi, and by the Lorenzetti brothers. The lat-ter, who died in 1348, probably victims of the plague, also worked in Florence, as can be seen here in some of their works which already seem influenced by Giotto's rigorous structural di-mensions. It is not surprising that Ambrogio was highly praised by the sculptor Lorenzo Ghi-berti for his achievements as artist, literary figure, philosopher, and lover of antiquity.

The works

1. PIETRO LORENZETTI
Madonna and Child enthroned with Angels
c. 1340
Tempera on wood
145x122
Inv. 1890 no. 445

2. AMBROGIO LORENZETTI
Madonna and Child with St. Nicholas and St. Proculus
1332
Tempera on wood
171x57 (central panel)
143x43 (side panels)
Inv. 1890 nos. 9411, 8731-8732

3. ANDREA VANNI
Madonna and Child
Late 14ᵗʰ century
Tempera on wood
87x67
Inv. 1890 no. 9476

4. SIMONE MARTINI AND LIPPO MEMMI
Annunciation
Signed and dated 1333
Tempera on wood
184x210
Inv. 1890 nos. 451-453
Restored: 2001

5. PIETRO LORENZETTI
Altarpiece of the Blessed Humility
c. 1340
Tempera on wood
51x21 (each pinnacle)
128x57 (central panel)
45x32 (each panel)
diam. 18 (tondoes)
Inv. 1890 nos. 8347, 6120-6126, 6129-6131

6. SIMONE DEI CROCIFISSI
Nativity
c. 1380
Tempera on wood
47x25
Inv. 1890 no. 3475

7. NICCOLÒ DI BONACCORSO
Presentation of the Virgin in the Temple
c. 1380
Tempera on wood
50x34
Inv. 1890 no. 3157

8. AMBROGIO LORENZETTI
Four stories from the life of St. Nicholas (Miracle of the poor youth and St. Nicholas consecrated as Bishop of Myra; Miracles of the possessed child and of the grain)
c. 1332
Tempera on wood
96x35 (each panel)
Inv. 1890 nos. 8348, 8349

9. AMBROGIO LORENZETTI
Presentation in the Temple
Signed and dated 1342
Tempera on wood
257x168
Inv. 1890 no. 8346
Restored: 1986

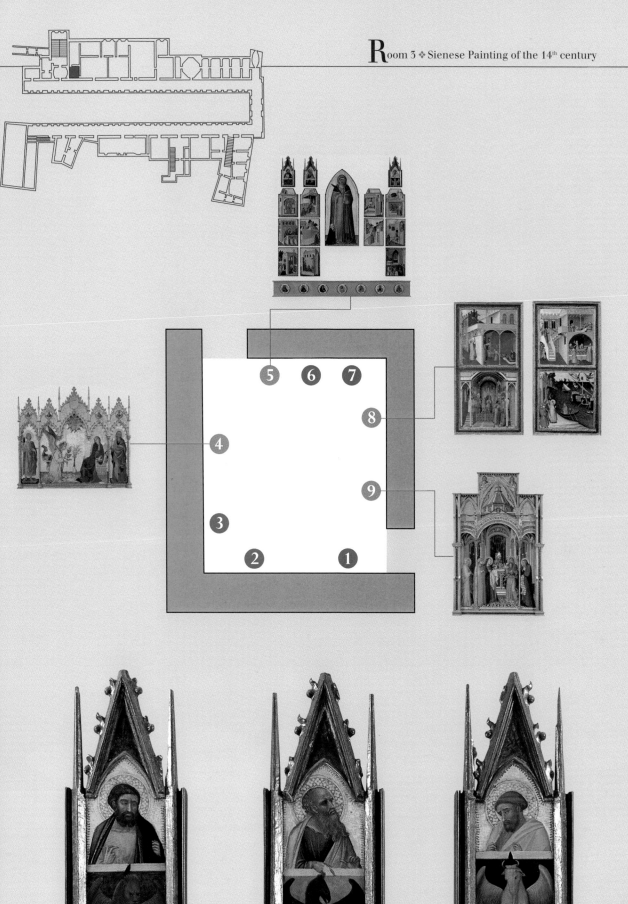

4

SIMONE MARTINI AND LIPPO MEMMI
Annunciation

This *Annunciation* was painted for the altar of Sant'Ansano in the Siena Cathedral and brought to the Uffizi by the Grand Duke Ferdinand III. The original frame is lost, but written beneath is an autograph documenting the date and the names of the painters, Simone Martini and his brother-in-law Lippo Memmi. On either side of the Annunciation are St. Ansano and Saint Juliette (or Saint Margaret). In the medallions above are the prophets Jeremiah, Ezechiel, Isaiah and Daniel, carrying scrolls which represent the Incarnation (the central tondo, now lost, was to overhang the dove of the Holy Spirit and represent God the Father). Typically Sienese in its fine use of gold and its linearity accentuated by the sinuous, timid withdrawal of the Virgin, the work also contains precious realistic detail such as the variegated marble paving, the chequered cloak of the angel, the sumptuous vase of lilies, and finally the foreshortened, half-open book. The writing across the painting produces an almost theatrical effect, indicating the greeting by the angel to the Virgin.

5

PIETRO LORENZETTI
Altarpiece of the Blessed Humility

Painted for the altar of the Blessed Humility in the church of St. John the Evangelist in Florence, dismantled into various parts (located in Berlin and elsewhere), the painting was reassembled in 1954 on the basis of an 18th century drawing. A benchmark of the mature work of Pietro Lorenzetti, here influenced by the quintessential solidity of the school of Giotto, the work represents eleven vivacious scenes from the miraculous life of the Blessed Humility, as she professes her hu-

mility (formerly known as Rosanese dei Negusanti, she was founder of the Vallombrosan convent of San Giovanni delle Donne of Faenza she died in 1310). At her feet, in the central panel, is perhaps Saint Margaret, second abbess of the monastery, who died in 1330. On the three surviving pinnacles are the evangelists Mark, John and Luke; on the predella are tondoes with a pietà of Christ, the Virgin and five saints. One of the scenes depicted, in which workers are rebuilding the roof of a church with a mule to carry the bricks, provides an interesting view of the life of the times.

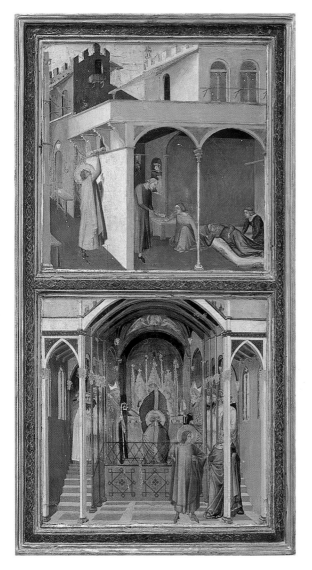 

8

AMBROGIO LORENZETTI
Four stories from the life of St. Nicholas
(*Miracle of the poor youth* and *St. Nicholas
consecrated as Bishop of Myra; Miracles
of the possessed child* and *of the grain*)

In the church of San Procolo in Florence, Ambrogio Lorenzetti completed a panel painting (perhaps the triptych with the *Madonna and Child, St. Nicholas and St. Proculous,* also in this room, Inv. nos. 9411, 8731-8732). He also painted "stories of St. Nicholas in small figures" in one of the church's chapels, a work which "enormously increased his name and reputation", as reported later by Vasari in 1568.

On the two panels with stories of St. Nicholas of Bari, part of a lost dossal or tabernacle, the Sienese painter proves himself not only a detailed story-teller, which would have been a striking quality for Florentines used to the simplicity of the Giottesque narrative style, but also an artist attentive to problems of space. A surprising vertical "fishbone" perspective is seen in the picture of the saint freeing the city of Myra from famine: in this marine landscape, the eye of the viewer is lifted up to the open sails along the horizon; note also the devices of portraying the saint from behind, and of the showing the clerks emerging from behind columns in the scene of the bishop's consecration.

AMBROGIO LORENZETTI
Presentation in the Temple

Painted for the altar of San Crescenzio in Siena Cathedral. The scene, with its complex setting which plays around the perspective lines of the paving, is much more attractive than the usu-al static figures of saints characteristic of altarpieces of the time. Its minute detail and the many descriptive and symbolic inscriptions invite our curiosity. The use of lacquer and costly lapis lazuli for the blue tones confirms the importance of the work, which was copied up until a century later by Sienese painters.

Room 4 ❖ Florentine Painting of the 14th century

Giotto's innovations – lifelike figures, luminosity and three-dimensional space effects in particular – influenced many artists working in Florence throughout the 14th century. Their work is represented here by a number of masterpieces coming mostly from Florentine churches. Great variety can be seen in the Giottesque school: Taddeo Gaddi, among the few artists to live beyond the mid-century point, was particularly attentive to perspective; Bernardo Daddi seems to have been more inspired by the works of Giotto's youth, while others, such as the Master of Saint Cecilia or Pacino di Bonaguida, tend toward miniaturist effects. Later, in the second half of the 14th century, Giottino and Giovanni da Milano show more "modern" tendencies as compared to the painting, conventional but highly esteemed at the time, of the Orcagna brothers.

The works

1. **GIOVANNI DA MILANO**
Ognissanti Polyptych
c. 1360
Tempera on wood
132x39 (panels), 49x39 (predellas)
Inv. 1890 no. 459

2. **ANDREA DI CIONE KNOW AS ORCAGNA AND JACOPO DI CIONE**
St. Matthew Triptych
c. 1367-1368
Tempera on wood
291x265
Inv. 1890 no. 3163
Restored: 1981

3. **BERNARDO DADDI**
San Pancrazio Polyptych
c. 1342
Tempera on wood
165x85 (central panel), 127x42 (side panels)
31x17 (pinnacles), diam. 20 (tondoes)
43x32 (predellas)
Inv. 1890 nos. 8458, 6127-28, 8345

4. **GIOTTINO**
Pietà
c. 1360-1365
Tempera on wood
195x134
Inv. 1890 no. 454

5. **TADDEO GADDI**
Madonna enthroned with Angels and Saints
1355
Tempera on wood
154x80
Dep. Inv. no. 3

6. **NARDO DI CIONE**
Crucifixion
c. 1350
Tempera on wood
145x71
Inv. 1890 no. 3515
Restored: 1994

7. **BERNARDO DADDI**
Madonna and Child with St. Matthew and St. Nicholas
1328
Tempera on wood
144x194
Inv. 1890 no. 3073

8. **BERNARDO DADDI**
Madonna enthroned with Angels and Saints
1334
Tempera on wood
56x26
Inv. 1890 no. 8564
Restored: 1994

9. **WORKSHOP OF PACINO DI BONAGUIDA** (below)
Crucifixion and Saints
14th century
Tempera on wood
12.5x39.5
Inv. 1890 no. 9919
Work acquired by Rodolfo Siviero

10. **JACOPO DEL CASENTINO** (above)
Madonna enthroned with Angels and Saints
Signed, c. 1340
Tempera on wood
39x42
Inv. 1890 no. 9528
Restored: 1992

11. **MASTER OF SAINT CECILIA**
Saint Cecilia and stories of her life
After 1304
Tempera on wood
85x181
Inv. 1890 no. 449

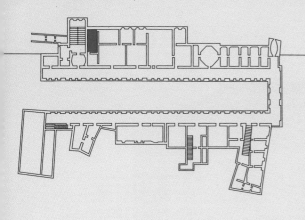

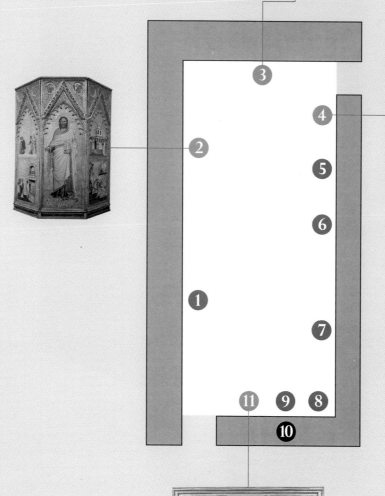

2

ANDREA DI CIONE KNOWN AS ORCAGNA AND JACOPO DI CIONE
St. Matthew Triptych

In 1367 the Bankers Guild commissioned Orcagna to paint a panel for the west pillar of its property in Orsanmichele, the seat of the Florentine Guilds. Considered to be among the best painters of his time and already a consultant for the works at the Cathedral, the artist became ill and the painting was completed by his brother Jacopo di Cione the following year. The unusual trapezoidal structure of the panel was created specifically for the pillar on which it was to hang. The central figure of St. Matthew is flanked by four small scenes (*Miracle of the dragons, Calling of the Saint, Resurrection of King Egippus' son, Martyrdom of the Saint*). Each scene is given an inscription. Above, the tondoes show the golden coins which symbolise the Bankers Guild. A work of great subtlety, it is enriched by details such as the rich brocade at the feet of the saint.

3

BERNARDO DADDI
San Pancrazio Polyptych

In 1568 Vasari attributed this polyptych, formerly on the main altar of the church of San Pancrazio, to another member of the Florentine School, Agnolo Gaddi. The central panel of the polyptych shows the traditional Madonna and Child enthroned with angels; to the sides are six panels with full-figure saints; above are fourteen small pinnacled panels with prophets and half-length portraits of saints and four tondoes with angels. On the predella are seven small panels with stories of the Virgin. Probably at least six other pieces are missing and possibly also another predella, mentioned by Vasari, with stories of Saint Reparata, the Florentine patroness. This is therefore one of the most spectacular polyptychs of its time, although Vasari preferred only the smaller parts: "The only part of it which is really good, is the predella, filled with small figures". Bernardo Daddi, amongst the most delightful of those representatives of the Giotto school who displayed miniaturistic tendencies, was in fact most at ease when narrating intimate, everyday scenes, peopled by graceful and lively figures.

4

GIOTTINO
Pietà

This panel painting, originally in the church of San Remigio, is considered one of the masterpieces of Florentine painting from the second half of the 14ᵗʰ century, for the rare psychological insight of the faces and for its luminous pictorial quality. Along with the traditional characters mourning at the Deposition of Christ are two female figures dressed in 14ᵗʰ century clothing: a Benedectine nun, and a young, sumptuously dressed woman; kneeling to participate in the sorrowful event, protected by the hands of the patron Sts. Benedict and Remigius. The artist was praised by Vasari for his "gentleness and sweetness", his varied facial expressions and emotions, and his imaginative qualities.

MASTER OF SAINT CECILIA
Saint Cecilia and stories of her life

The fire which destroyed the church of Santa Cecilia in 1304 was recorded by the fourteenth-century chronicler Giovanni Villani; the church was rebuilt immediately afterwards and there is a convincing school of thought which holds that this altarpiece, among the most remarkable examples of the early fourteenth century Florentine School, was painted for this church just after the fire. It portrays Saint Cecilia enthroned, flanked by eight stories of her life, ending with her martyrdom. The scenes, characterised by a minutely detailed realism, echo Giotto's frescoes in the upper church at Assisi. In this early evocation of the experiments of the young Giotto, however, the three-dimensional effect is still clearly in an experimental phase (note for example, top left, the carefully-prepared table for the wedding banquet of Cecilia and Valerian). Other works have also been attributed to this unknown contemporary of Giotto, this master whose name comes from the altarpiece in the Uffizi: scenes from the life of St. Francis in the frescoes of the upper church in Assisi and several panel paintings from the churches of San Giorgio alla Costa, San Simone and Santa Margherita a Montici in Florence.

This room, lit up by a great skylight, is dominated by two majestic altarpieces, the Adoration of the Magi *by Gentile da Fabriano and the* Coronation of the Virgin *by Lorenzo Monaco. The arrangement was carried out in the late Fifties within the context of the reorganization, considered a milestone in modern museology, of the rooms dedicated to Medieval and early 13th century art. The moment of transition from Late Gothic to Early Renaissance art, distinguished by special attention to rich colors and a new study of movement in bodies, is represented here by Agnolo Gaddi, known also as the "chapel decorator" of the Santa Croce Basilica. Along with Gentile da Fabriano, who came from the Marches region and was the favorite artist of the wealthy and highly cultured Palla Strozzi, the most outstanding personalities in this culture reaching into the new century remain Lorenzo Monaco, a confirmed master of large paintings as well as illuminated manuscripts, and Gherardo Starnina, a still enigmatic personage who also worked in the Iberian peninsula, and who may perhaps be identified with the so-called Master of the Lively Child.* The Thebaide, *now attributed to Fra Angelico, was once believed to be a work by Starnina.*

The works

**1. LORENZO MONACO
AND COSIMO ROSSELLI**
Adoration of the Magi
c.1420-1422
Tempera on wood
115x170
Inv. 1890 no. 466
Restored: 1995

2. GIOVANNI DI PAOLO
Madonna and Child with Saints
Signed and dated 1445
Tempera on wood
247x212
Inv. 1890 no. 3255

3. AGNOLO GADDI
Crucifixion
c. 1390
Tempera on wood; 59x77
Inv. 1890 no. 464
Restored: 1997

4. JACOPO BELLINI
Madonna and Child
c. 1450
Tempera on wood; 69x49
Inv. 1890 no. 3344
Restored: 1988

5. GENTILE DA FABRIANO
Adoration of the Magi
1423
Tempera on wood
300x283 (total), 173x220 (panel)
Inv. 1890 no. 8364
Restored: 2004

6. GENTILE DA FABRIANO
*Four Saints
from the Quaratesi Polyptych*
1422-1425

Tempera on wood
200x60 (each panel)
Inv. 1890 no. 887
Restored: 2001

7. LORENZO MONACO
*Coronation
of the Virgin*
1414
(signed and dated
1413 according
to the Florentine style)
Tempera on wood
450x350
Inv. 1890 no. 885
Restored: 1998

**8. GHERARDO STARNINA
(MASTER OF THE
LIVELY CHILD)**
Madonna and Child
First decade
of the 15th century
Tempera on wood
79x52
Inv. 1890 no. 6270
Restored: 1995

9. FRA ANGELICO
The Thebaide
1420
Tempera on wood
80x216
Inv. 1890 no. 447

10. MASOLINO
Virgin of Humility
1430-1435
Tempera on wood
110.5x62
Inv. 1890 no. 9922
Work acquired
by Rodolfo Siviero

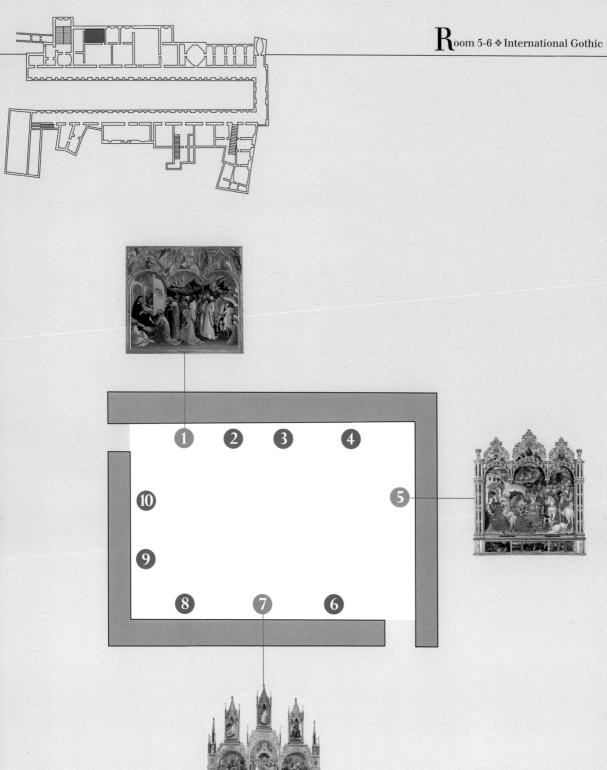

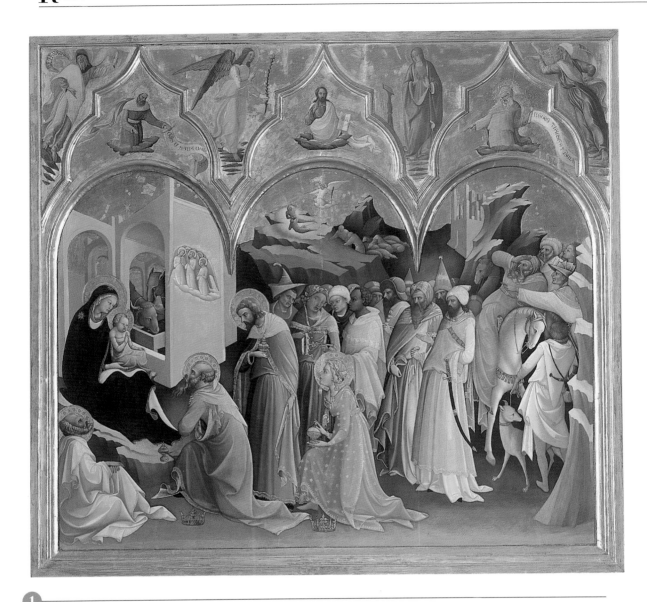

① LORENZO MONACO AND COSIMO ROSSELLI
Adoration of the Magi

The provenance of this panel painting is uncertain, but it is probably the altarpiece painted for the church of Sant'Egidio by Don Lorenzo, a Camaldolese monk from Santa Maria degli Angeli. It is probable that the occasion for this was the reconsecration of that church by Pope Martin V, an event of great importance at the time. Originally there may well have been a predella, now lost, such as in the contemporary *Adoration of the Magi* painted by Gentile da Fabriano. Lorenzo Monaco, also a fine miniaturist, was the founder of a stylistic reformation which, starting from the experiences of the Giotto school, created lively figures displaying movement in every part of the body. Exotic devices stand out from the painting, such as the inscriptions in pseudo-Kufic (ancient Arabic) characters on the cloak of the standing Magus and the nearby figure, between the three pinnacles depicting Christ bestowing blessings and two prophets, Cosimo Rosselli added two more prophets and the two figures of the Annunciation, transforming the tricuspid altarpiece into a rectangular one, more consonant with Renaissance style. Recent restoration has revealed the brilliant colours obtained with lacquer and lapis lazuli.

5

GENTILE DA FABRIANO
Adoration of the Magi

Palla Strozzi, man of learning and great wealth, a rival of the Medici who was once exiled to Padua, commissioned this sumptuous work for his family chapel in the church of Santa Trinita, where he planned the building of a public library with Greek and Latin volumes. His humanist education with Byzantine influences is reflected in this work by Gentile da Fabriano, who was by 1420 living in Florence as a tenant of Palla Strozzi. With its rich use of gold, applied to the panel in relief, the painting was to represent publicly the affluence and culture of the client, and to echo the words of Leonardo Bruni, Chancellor of the Republic: "The possession of external wealth affords the occasion to exercise virtue". The Adoration in the centre of the panel is simply the culminating moment of the fabulous procession of the Magi, which winds its way down from the top of the panel, beneath a night sky illuminated by the star of Bethlehem. The eye is drawn to many details: from the numerous flowers, all drawn from nature, to the small pillars, to the fabrics woven with gold, and the harnesses of the horses. This analytical intensity of detail would seem to correspond to the literary style typical of Greek humanism, the so-called *ékphrasis*, which allows the minute, elaborate description of multiple elements.

7

LORENZO MONACO
Coronation of the Virgin

This monumental altarpiece, painted in Florence for the high altar of Santa Maria degli Angeli, mother church of the Camaldolensian Order, was completed by the painter monk in February 1414. The inscription on the frame above the predella bearing the date 1413 is based on the old Florentine calendar, in which the year started in March. The crowned Virgin is portrayed surrounded by a throng of saints, suspended above a fantastic rainbow whose shades of blue allude to the starry heavens. On the pinnacles are Christ the Saviour, an angel and the Virgin after the Annunciation. On the predella, beside the Nativity and the Adoration of the Magi, are episodes from the life of St. Benedict, whose rule was followed by the Camaldolensian monks. "Worked with great ornament" as reported by Antonio Billi in the early 16th century, the painting was replaced at the end of the century, in harmony with late 16th century taste, by a great canvas by Alessandro Allori (Accademia Gallery). Found again in the 19th century in the Camaldolensian Abbey of San Piero a Cerreto, severely damaged by the infiltration of water and the loss of much of its sumptuous woodwork, the altarpiece underwent extensive restoration in 1990, which has brought out its brilliant, precious colours deriving from a generous use of lapis lazuli.

Room 7 ❖ The Early Renaissance

A new conception of the dialogue between men, and then of man's relationship with God: this is in brief the humanistic idea that permeates the work of Masaccio, whose Saint Anne Metterza, *painted still in collaboration with Masolino, provides an ideal opening to the itinerary of this extraordinary room, where some of the great masterpieces of the early Renaissance exemplify the new research in perspective and lighting effects carried out by Fra Angelico, Paolo Uccello, and Domenico Veneziano, as well as the keen psychological studies of Piero della Francesca, the sensitive interpreter of a renewed inspiration by antiquity.*

The works

1. Paolo Uccello
Battle of San Romano
c. 1438
Tempera on wood
182x220
Inv. 1890 no. 479

2. Piero della Francesca
Diptych of the Duke and Duchess of Urbino (Portraits of Battista Sforza and Federigo da Montefeltro; Triumphal carriages, rear panel)
c. 1467-1470
Tempera on wood
47x33 (each)
Inv. 1890 nos. 3342, 1615
Restored: 1986

3. Masaccio
Madonna and Child
c. 1426
Tempera on wood
24.5x18.2
Inv. 1890 no. 9929
Work acquired
by Rodolfo Siviero

4. Masaccio e Masolino
Saint Anne Metterza
c. 1424
Tempera on wood
175x103
Inv. 1890 no. 8386

5. Domenico Veneziano
Santa Lucia dei Magnoli Altarpiece
c. 1445
Tempera on wood
209x216
Inv. 1890 no. 884

6. Beato Angelico
Madonna and Child
(the so-called *Pontassieve Madonna*)
c. 1435
Tempera on wood
134x59
Dep. Inv. no. 143

7. Beato Angelico
Coronation of the Virgin
c. 1435
Tempera on wood
112x114
Inv. 1890 no. 1612

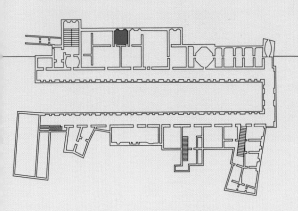

PAOLO UCCELLO
The Battle of San Romano

Along with two panels in London and Paris, that of the Uffizi forms part of a cycle portraying different stages of the Battle of San Romano, where in Valdelsa the Florentines defeated the Duke of Milan, ally of the Sienese and the Emperor in 1432. In 1492 an inventory of the belongings of Lorenzo the Magnificent listed this painting as existing in Palazzo Medici, and this was thought to be its original provenance, having been commissioned by Cosimo the Elder. An important discovery by Francesco Caglioti has now put an end to a discordant whirl of hy-

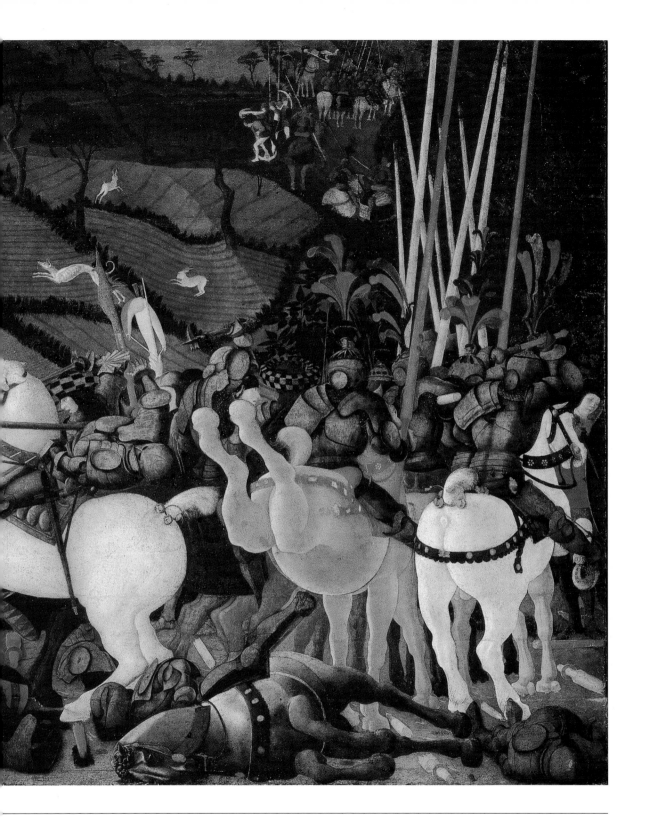

potheses on the dating of the cycle. Its intriguing history, only briefly outlined here, has been traced on the basis of incontrovertible archival data. The series was painted for a certain Bartolini, perhaps Lionardo, a leading figure in Florentine politics, who refurnished his home in Porta Rossa around 1438. After some decades the three panels, trans-ferred to the family residence at Santa Maria a Quinto by the heirs, were forcefully acquired by Lorenzo the Magnificent from the brothers Andrea and Damiano Bartolini. The latter, after a "long and never resolved dispute", managed to get them back again in 1495. In the 16th century they returned once more to the Medici family.

PIERO DELLA FRANCESCA
*Diptych of the Duchess
and Duke of Urbino* (front)

In the 15th century, as in antiquity, the diptych was considered a particularly precious work and was originally joined by a hinge, to be opened like a book or on occasion to be presented as a gift. Painted on both sides (on the outer were the allegorical *Triumphs* of the two personages in the carriages, shown here on the first page of Room 7), the famous diptych of Urbino, formerly in the Audience Hall in the Ducal Palace, arrived in Florence in 1631 with the inheritance of Vittoria Della Rovere, wife of the Grand Duke Ferdinand II. On the front are the Duke and Duchess of Urbino facing one another in solemn profile, in the classical medallion style which was very much in vogue during the humanistic period.

The precision of the features, focusing even on the less attractive details such as Federigo's nose, broken during a tournament, is a typical characteristic of Flemish art and confirms that Piero della Francesca (active in the court of Urbino) was one of the most sensitive interpreters of Nordic art, which was at that time well-known and popular from Ferrara to Florence and Urbino, right down to the south of Italy. Even the tidy landscape in the background, fading towards the distant hills and the horizon, possibly evoking the territory of Montefeltro, the Duke's land, is treated with an almost miniaturistic technique. Without using the traditional expedient of a curtain or window, the magnificent bird's-eye view unites the perspective of the two panels. The great painter from Sansepolcro was also in fact the author of important theoretical treatises on perspective, such as the *De Prospectiva pingendi*.

④

MASACCIO AND MASOLINO
Saint Anne Metterza

This work, formerly in the church of Sant'Ambrogio was the fruit of a collaboration between Masolino and his younger countryman Masaccio. Saint Anne and the angels are generally attributed to Masolino, with the exception of that on the top right of the painting, probably done by Masaccio, who was also responsible for the Virgin with Child. The symbolic meaning of this altarpiece is, despite the simplicity of its composition, quite complex. It is not known under what circumstances the work was commissioned. The three main figures, Saint Anne, the Virgin and the Child, placed along the same axis, have the static quality of Byzantine Madonnas (but the plasticity of the figures is entirely of 15th century, and the angel swinging the censer introduces a sense of movement). According to new theories, the panel may have been placed within a great devotional ciborium in the church of Sant'Ambrogio. In similar vein to the later *Coronation* by Filippo Lippi, originally situated in the same church and now in the Uffizi (Room 8), this work, inspired by the cults of Corpus Domini and the Immaculate Conception venerated in Sant'Ambrogio, represents the concept of a benevolent authority exercised by the Church within Christian society. The title of the work, *Saint Anne Metterza* (from the Medieval latin "met", the same, and "tertius", the third), is normally used in art history to refer to representations of the mother of the Virgin with her daughter and the Child sitting between her knees. In this painting Saint Anne acquires a key symbolic value, and probably also alludes to the historical figure of the abbess of the convent. To the faithful she represents a mother who protects a daughter who is without sin and who is the progenitress of the body of Christ. It is no mere fancy that the scholar Roberto Longhi should have recognised the silhouette of Brunelleschi's cupola in the open arms of the saint, as they lean upon Mary's shoulders in a gesture of protection. For the cupola itself, "climbing steeply to the skies", "wide enough to cover the whole of the Tuscan people with its shadow", as the great architect Leon Battista Alberti wrote in the 15th century, clasps the city of Florence in an ideal embrace.

51

5

DOMENICO VENEZIANO
Santa Lucia dei Magnoli Altarpiece

Formerly in the church of Santa Lucia dei Magnoli, the altarpiece is today without its extraordinary predella, which has been dismantled and divided amongst the museums of Washington, Cambridge and Berlin. Its innovative use of light makes it one of the masterpieces of its time. Instead of the traditional Medieval triptych, the sacred conversation takes place within a harmonious architectural structure of three arches with inlaid marble on the façade, rendered still more delicate by the pastel tones of rose and green, and enriched by a multicoloured pavement in receding squares. The morning light is emphasised by the shadow falling on the Virgin and Child. The branches of a citrus orchard stand out against an intensely realistic sky. In the foreground are St. Francis, St. John the Baptist, St. Zanobius (patron of Florence, wearing rich costume with fabric and jewels of the era) and Saint Lucia, to whom the church was dedicated. The Venetian painter died in poverty in Florence, his chosen city.

7

BEATO ANGELICO
Coronation of the Virgin

At the beginning of the 16ᵗʰ century, a description by the Anonimo Gaddiano places this panel by Giovanni da Fiesole, otherwise known as Fra Angelico, in the church of Sant'Egidio in the Hospital of Santa Maria Nuova, "where Paradise is painted". Fra Angelico painted another *Coronation* with a different composition (now in the Louvre) possibly just before this, for the church of the convent of San Domenico below Fiesole, where he lived for a long time. The work in the Uffizi, which probably formed a whole with two predellas now in the Museum of San Marco (*Wedding* and *Funeral of the Virgin*), is intensely illuminated by a profusion of gold and clever use of light; its perspective is created by a series of small clouds which drift into the background. Surrounding the scene of the *Coronation*, emphasised by the "firework" effect of a burst of golden rays, is a great circle of saints and angels (note the impact of the trumpets crossing over each other).

53

Room 8 ❖ Lippi

This room, inaugurated in 1997 after major reorganization, forms part of the section, annexed to the Gallery in the late 19th century, that was originally occupied by the Medicean Theatre designed by Buontalenti in 1586 for Francesco I de' Medici. As in Room 15, dedicated to Leonardo, the paintings are now softly lit from above by a vast skylight in the ceiling. Along with a basic core of works by Filippo Lippi, a major figure in Florentine painting in the first half of the 15th century, are some masterpieces by his son Filippino, born of the Carmelite monk's relationship with the nun Lucrezia Buti. Among the works by Filippino are the imposing Altarpiece dated 1486, transferred here from Palazzo Vecchio, and an Adoration of the Child whose recent restoration has brought out brilliant shades of blue, restoring to the painting its original intense luminosity. The work of Alesso Baldovinetti, author of a book of memoirs, now lost, and vivacious experimenter in different techniques (fresco, stained glass, inlay, mosaic, engraving, goldsmithery) is also represented here.

The works

1. FILIPPO LIPPI
Madonna with Child and two Angels
c. 1465
Tempera on wood
95x63.5
Inv. 1890 no. 1598

2. FILIPPO LIPPI (above)
The Novitiate Altarpiece (Madonna and Child enthroned with Sts. Francis, Damian, Cosmas and Antony of Padua)
c. 1445
Tempera on wood
196x196
Inv. 1890 no. 8354

3. PESELLINO (below)
Predella of the Novitiate Altarpiece: St. Francis receiving the stigmata (copy of the original in the Louvre); *Miracle of Sts. Cosmas and Damian* (copy of the original in the Louvre); *Nativity; Martyrdom of Sts. Cosmas and Damian; Miracle of St. Antony*
c. 1441-1450
Tempera on wood
32x244
Inv. 1890 no. 8355

4. FILIPPO LIPPI
Camaldoli Adoration (Adoration of the Child with Sts. John and Romualdus)
c. 1463
Tempera on wood
140x130
Inv. 1890 no. 8353

5. FILIPPO LIPPI AND ASSISTANCE
Coronation of the Virgin
c. 1439-1447
Tempera on wood
200x287, diam. 21 (tondoes)
Inv. 1890 no. 8352
Restored: 1978

6. FILIPPO LIPPI
Adoration of the Child with Sts. Jerome, Hilarion, Joseph, Mary Magdalene and Angels
c. 1455
Tempera on wood
137x134
Inv. 1890 no. 8350

7. FILIPPO LIPPI (above)
Virgin after the Annunciation, Announcing Angel, St. Anthony Abbot, St. John the Baptist
c. 1450
Tempera on wood
57x24 (each panel)
Inv. 1890 nos. 8356-8357

8. FILIPPO LIPPI (below)
Predella of the Barbadori Altarpiece (the *Altarpiece* is in the Louvre, Paris)
c. 1437
Tempera on wood
40x235
Inv. 1890 no. 8351

9. ALESSO BALDOVINETTI
Annunciation
c. 1457
Tempera on wood
167x137
Inv. 1890 no. 483

10. ALESSO BALDOVINETTI
Madonna and Child with Saints
c. 1455
Tempera on wood
176x166
Inv. 1890 no. 487

11. FILIPPINO LIPPI AND ASSISTANCE
Adoration of the Magi
Signed and dated on the back 1496
Grease tempera on wood
258x243
Inv. 1890 no. 1566
Restored: 1985

12. FILIPPINO LIPPI
Madonna and Child with Saints
1486 (signed and dated February 20th 1485 according to the Florentine style)
Tempera on wood
355x255
Inv. 1890 no. 1568

13. FILIPPINO LIPPI
St. Jerome
c. 1485
Tempera on wood
136x71
Inv. 1890 no. 8652

14. FILIPPINO LIPPI
Adoration of the Child
c. 1480-1485
Tempera on wood
96x71
Inv. 1890 no. 3246
Restored: 1999

FILIPPO LIPPI
Madonna with Child and two Angels

This painting is today among the most admired in the Gallery. The Madonna, her hair entwined with precious pearls, has an enchanting profile, believed to be that of Lucrezia Buti, a nun beloved by the friar/painter who was to give him a daugh-ter and a son, Filippino, the future painter. The group, which also inspired Botticelli, Lippi's assistant in Prato, stands out from its frame with a delicacy similar to the classical-style reliefs of Donatello and Luca della Robbia.

The background, a painting-within-a-painting, seems to anticipate the expansive landscapes of Leonardo.

S·FRANCSC?·SDAMIANVS·   SCSMS·SANTONIVS·DEPA

FILIPPO LIPPI
The Novitiate Altarpiece

In 1445 Michelozzo, architect of Cosimo the Elder, completed the Novitiate Chapel in the Franciscan Basilica of Santa Croce.

For ornamenting the altar, Cosimo called on Filippo Lippi whose patron he was (he may have written this apology for the transgressive friar/painter: "Great minds are heavenly forms and not dray horses for hire").

The architectural background of the altarpiece has a classical structure, in tune with Michelozzo's taste. The red Medicean emblems on the top of the frieze and the marble of the pavement enliven the composition with chromatic highlights, in an almost Flemish manner.

It represents the Madonna enthroned with Child and Saints, also seated: from left to right, Francis (patron of Santa Croce), Cosmas and Damian (Medici patron saints) and St. Anthony of Padua.

5

FILIPPO LIPPI AND ASSISTANCE
Coronation of the Virgin

This was previously in Sant'Ambrogio, on the main altar restored by the prior Francesco Maringhi in 1441. Lippi's payments for the work began in 1439. Various painters collaborated in this undertaking: Piero di Lorenzo, Bartolomeo di Giovanni Corradini da Urbino, Fra Diamante, a young disciple of Lippi, and at least two able carpenters, Manno de' Cori and Domenico del Brilla. The original composition of the frame is lost and part of the predella is in a Berlin museum. In 1446 the altarpiece was transferred to the painter's home in the convent of Sant'Apollonia where the blue pigment used to finish the painting was available, and one year later to Sant'Ambrogio. Considerable amazement must have been provoked by the crowded scene of the *Coronation of the Virgin*. The cerimony takes place in heaven, as is perhaps suggested by the intense, diagonal strips in blue and azure. Among the characters, at the extreme left stands St. Ambrose; kneeling below is the presumed self-portrait of the friar who looks out at the spectator with a bored air; in the centre is St. Eustace with his two small sons and wife Theophista; to the right is the donor next to the inscription IS PERFECIT OPUS ("He finished the work").

9

ALESSO BALDOVINETTI
Annunciation

In this work, commissioned by the Silvestrine monks for the church of San Giorgio alla Costa, the *Annunciation* takes place in a scenario of refined classical architecture against a lovely, airy background with a flower-strewn meadow and tall trees behind a wall. The Florentine artist, who experimented with new techniques in the use of warm, mellow colors such as the red of the arches in this picture, seems more interested in the elegant setting of the holy scene than its spirituality.

FILIPPINO LIPPI AND ASSISTANCE
Adoration of the Magi

In 1496 Filippino Lippi, with the aid of other artists, painted this *Adoration* for the Augustinian convent of San Donato in Scopeto, to replace one which was never finished by Leonardo. Among the contemporary portraits included in the sacred event, to the left are the Medici "Popolani": the old man kneeling with the astrolabe, which alludes to the "astronomer" Wise Kings, is Pierfrancesco di Lorenzo; behind him are his sons Lorenzo, Lord of Piombino, and Giovanni, who in 1496 was ambassador to Caterina Sforza, by whom he was to have Lodovico, the future condottiere Giovanni dalle Bande Nere and father of Cosimo I. The three characters portrayed are from the Medici line which relinquished its power in fidelity to the Republic of Savonarola: here the crown is taken from Giovanni's head while his brother offers him a precious cup to present to the Child Jesus.

FILIPPINO LIPPI
Madonna with Child and Saints

Previously in the Council Hall of Palazzo Vecchio, this work was bought for 1,200 lire at the wish of Lorenzo de' Medici. Some artisans collaborated with Filippino Lippi on the frame and on the curtain which was to veil the panel on the altar. The saints who flank the Madonna enthroned and crowned by angels, confirm the civic importance of the painting: John the Baptist and Victor, patrons of Florence and of the Guelph party; Bernard, on whose book is the word "medica", perhaps an implicit reference to the Medici family; and Zanobius, patron of the diocese, wearing a jewel on his cloak displaying the red lily, a symbol of Florence.

Room 9 ❖ Pollaiolo

In addition to the Cardinal of Portugal's Altarpiece *– precious testimony to the eclectic workshop of Antonio del Pollaiolo and his younger brother Piero – this room contains the series of six* Virtues *(of which* Prudence, Justice *and* Charity *have recently been restored) commissioned of Piero by the Merchant's Guild in 1469, and then continued by Botticelli with his* Fortitude, *also recently restored.*
Other interesting works are the portraits and paintings of small size dedicated to Biblical and Mythological themes.

The works

1. PIERO DEL POLLAIOLO
Portrait of Galeazzo
Maria Sforza
1471
Tempera on wood
65x42
Inv. 1890 no. 1492
Restored: 1994

2. ANTONIO AND PIERO DEL POLLAIOLO
Cardinal of Portugal's
Altarpiece
1466-1468
Oil on wood
172x179
Inv. 1890 no. 1617
Restored: 1994

3. FILIPPINO LIPPI (ATTR.)
Portrait of Youth
with red hat
Last decades
of 15th century
Oil on wood
53x35
Inv. 1890 no. 1490

4. ANTONIO DEL POLLAIOLO
Portrait of a Woman
c. 1475
Tempera on wood
55x34
Inv. 1890 no. 1491

5. SANDRO BOTTICELLI
The discovery of the body
of Holophernes;
The return of Judith
c. 1470-1472
Tempera on wood
31x24 and 31x25
Inv. 1890 nos. 1484, 1487

6. ANTONIO DEL POLLAIOLO
Hercules and the Hydra;
Hercules and Antaeus
c. 1475
Grease tempera on wood
17x12 and 16x9
Inv. 1890 nos. 8268, 1478
Restored: 1991

7. JACOPO DEL SELLAIO
The banquet of Ahasuerus
c. 1490
Tempera on wood; 45x63
Inv. 1890 no. 491

8. SANDRO BOTTICELLI
Fortitude
1470
Tempera on wood; 167x87
Inv. 1890 no. 1606
Restored: 1998

9. PIERO DEL POLLAIOLO
Temperance
c. 1470
Grease tempera on wood
167x88
Inv. 1890 no. 497
Restored: 1999

10. PIERO DEL POLLAIOLO
Prudence
c. 1470
Grease tempera on wood
167x88
Inv. 1890 no. 1610
Restored: 2000

11. PIERO DEL POLLAIOLO
Justice
c. 1470
Grease tempera on wood
167x88
Inv. 1890 no. 496
Restored: 2001

12. PIERO DEL POLLAIOLO
Faith
c. 1470
Grease tempera on wood
167x88
Inv. 1890 no. 498
Restored: 1999

13. PIERO DEL POLLAIOLO
Hope
c. 1470
Grease tempera on wood
167x88
Inv. 1890 no. 495

14. PIERO DEL POLLAIOLO
Charity
1469
Grease tempera on wood
167x88
Inv. 1890 no. 499
Restored: 2003

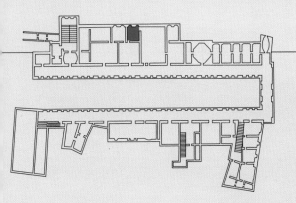

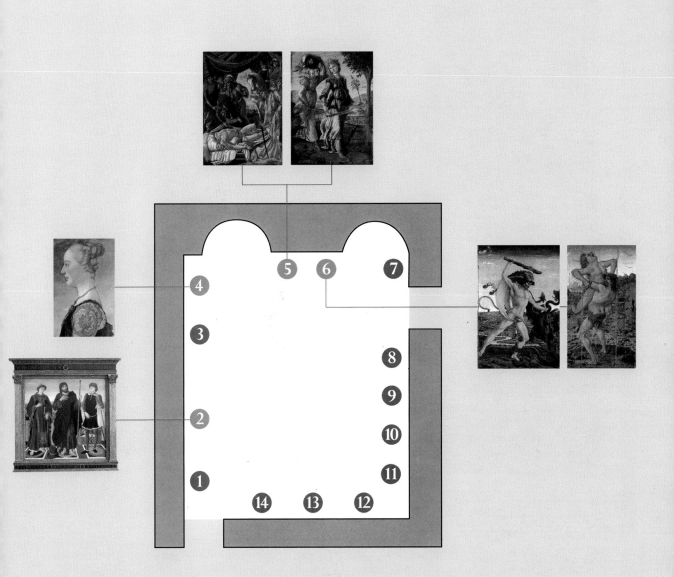

VOBIS DATVM EST NOSE◉MIS TERIVM RENGNI DEI

Ƨ VINCENTIVS ◉ ·Ƨ IACOBVS·AP ◉ Ƨ· EVSTACIVS

ANTONIO AND PIERO DEL POLLAIOLO
Cardinal of Portugal's Altarpiece

This work comes from the altar of the Cardinal of Portugal's chapel in San Miniato al Monte. It has been replaced with a copy. The chapel, on which the major artists of that time worked, among them Baldovinetti and Della Robbia, is dedicated to Jacob of Lusitania, Cardinal of Lisbon, who died in Florence in 1459, aged 25. The Pollaiolo brothers ran a prolific Florentine workshop dealing in painting, sculpture and goldsmithery. Their altarpiece, made of oak, has been given an unusual oily priming, typical of Flemish art. The work displays the fascination of the period for richly varied compositions: it is magnificent in its garments studded with jewels, the landscape which one glimpses beyond the balustrade and the variegated marble paving. In the centre of the hat the pilgrims' shell can be seen at the feet of St. Jacob of Compostela, the patron saint of pilgrims.

4

ANTONIO DEL POLLAIOLO
Portrait of a Woman

The woman is portrayed in a half-bust profile on a rich background of blue lapis lazuli. Around her neck is a pearl necklace with a particular-ly beautiful pendent, which shows an angel in relief overlying a large ruby. She is wearing a head-dress typical of 15th century Florentine ladies: a veil covers her ears and the "honey-comb" plait in her golden hair is delicately high-lighted by pearls.

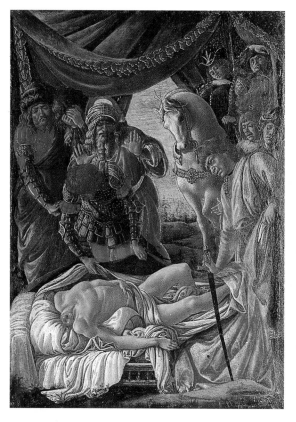

5

SANDRO BOTTICELLI
The discovery of the body of Holofernes
The return of Judith

Previously part of a precious diptych with a carved and gilded walnut frame (now lost), the panels were documented in 1584 as a gift from the collector Ridolfo Sirigatti to the Grand Duchess Bianca Cappello, second wife of Francesco I; they were then passed down to her son, Don Antonio de' Medici, who lived in the Casino in Via Larga from 1588. Judith, a Biblical heroin, is the model of feminine virtue and of justice bringing victory to the weak, and had already been recalled as such by Boccaccio in *De claris mulieribus*. The diptych comes from Botticelli's early years; while showing the influence of Pollaiolo in the perfect integration of figure and landscape, it is already clearly original in the knowledgeable combinations of colours and in the use of light to illuminate clothing as well as the bedsheet on which the decapitated corpse of Holofernes sprawls, a splendid nude study.

6

ANTONIO DEL POLLAIOLO
Hercules and the Hydra
Hercules and Antaeus

Around 1460 Pollaiolo painted three large canvasses of the *Labours of Hercules* for the Palazzo Medici. They were commissioned by Cosimo the Elder or perhaps his son, Piero (but not by the 11-year-old Lorenzo de' Medici, as some have claimed).
The paintings may be part of a cycle on defeated tyranny (the character of Hercules, defender of order and justice and a legendary symbol of Florence, does in fact represent both political and religious virtues). The two panels from the Uffizi, with a third piece in a private collection on which Antonio's brother Piero collaborated, are most probably smaller copies, also by Pollaiolo, of the lost cycle. The sculptural, dynamic tension of the bodies is typical of Antonio del Pollaiolo, who is famous for his studies of nude and anatomy.

Room 10-14 ❖ Botticelli

This room, created in 1943 from the upper part of the Medici Theatre, houses the foremost collection of Botticelli in the world. An initial layout was created in the postwar period with the altarpieces of Filippino Lippi, Perugino and Signorelli. In the 1950s works by Botticelli were transferred here, and by 1978 the layout was as we see it today, apart from one or two transfers in the early 1990s. Botticelli's formation as an artist is displayed here through both sacred and profane works: from the early works which still show the influence of Filippo Lippi, Verrocchio and Pollaiolo, to those conceived in the intellectual circle of the Medici, to the mystic paintings of his mature years. Other cultural tendencies of the age are represented in this room by Ghirlandaio, an artist receptive to Flemish painting, which in turn is also represented here by the large Triptych of Van der Goes.

The works

1. SANDRO BOTTICELLI
St. Augustine in his study
Variously dated from 1490 to 1500
Tempera on wood
41x27
Inv. 1890 no. 1473

2. SANDRO BOTTICELLI
Madonna of the Rose Garden
c. 1470
Tempera on wood
124x64
Inv. 1890 no. 1601
Restored: 1994

3. SANDRO BOTTICELLI
Madonna of the Magnificat
Variously dated from 1481 to 1485
Tempera on wood
Diam. 118
Inv. 1890 no. 1609
Restored: 1981

4. SANDRO BOTTICELLI
The birth of Venus
c. 1484
Tempera on linen
172.5x278.5
Inv. 1890 no. 878
Restored: 1987

5. SANDRO BOTTICELLI
Pallas and the Centaur
c. 1482
Tempera on linen
207x148
Dep. Inv. no. 29

6. SANDRO BOTTICELLI
Madonna in glory with Cherubim
c. 1469-1470
Tempera on wood
120x66
Inv. 1890 no. 504
Restored: 1995

7. SANDRO BOTTICELLI
Madonna of the Pomegranate
c. 1487
Tempera on wood; diam. 143.5
Inv. 1890 no. 1607

8. SANDRO BOTTICELLI
Calumny
c. 1495
Tempera on wood; 62x91
Inv. 1890 no. 1496
Restored: 2003

9. SANDRO BOTTICELLI
Primavera (Spring)
c. 1482
Grease tempera on wood; 203x314
Inv. 1890 no. 8360
Restored: 1982

10. SANDRO BOTTICELLI
Adoration of the Magi
c. 1475
Tempera on wood; 111x134
Inv. 1890 no. 882
Restored: 1980

11. SANDRO BOTTICELLI
Portrait of a Youth with a medal
c. 1470-1475
Tempera on wood and gilded
plaster mould (the medal); 56.5x44
Inv. 1890 no. 1488
Restored: 1991

12. SANDRO BOTTICELLI
Sant'Ambrogio Altarpiece
(or of the Converted Sisters)
c. 1467-1470
Tempera on wood; 170x194
Inv. 1890 no. 8657
Restored: 1992

13. DOMENICO GHIRLANDAIO
Adoration of the Magi
Dated 1487
Tempera on wood; diam. 172
Inv. 1890 no. 1619
Restored: 2002

14. HUGO VAN DER GOES
The Portinari Triptych
c. 1477-1478
Oil on wood
253x304 (central panel)
253x141 (side panels)
Inv. 1890 nos. 3191-3193

15. DOMENICO GHIRLANDAIO
Madonna enthroned
with Angels and Saints
In the predella:
Christ as the Man of Sorrows
and *Stories of Saints*
c. 1485
Tempera on wood
168x197 (altarpiece)
10.5x220 (predella)
Inv. 1890 nos. 8388, 8387
Restored: 1981

16. DOMENICO GHIRLANDAIO
Madonna enthroned
with Angels and Saints
c. 1484
Tempera on wood
191x200
Inv. 1890 no. 881
Restored: 1981

17. SANDRO BOTTICELLI
Annunciation
c. 1489
Tempera on wood
150x156
Inv. 1890 no. 1608
Restored: 1987

18. SANDRO BOTTICELLI
San Marco Altarpiece
(Coronation of the Virgin)
c. 1488-1490
Tempera on wood
375x256
Inv. 1890 no. 8362
Restored: 1990

19. SANDRO BOTTICELLI
St. Barnabas Altarpiece
c. 1488
Tempera on wood
340x279
Inv. 1890 no. 8361
Restored: 2002

SANDRO BOTTICELLI
Madonna of the Magnificat

This famous tondo, in which the figures appear as if reflected in a convex mirror, against a serene fluvial landscape in the distance, takes its title from the beginning of the prayer indicated by the Christ Child on the right-hand page of the open book: *Magnificat anima mea* are in fact the first words of the canticle sung by Mary in praise of the Lord on her visit to Elizabeth, the wife of Zacchariah, who is expecting a child, as narrated in St. Luke's Gospel (I. 46). There may be an allusion to this same episode on the left-hand page of the book, with Zaccharia's prophecy on the birth of his son John the Baptist (Luke, I, 76-79), who was to be the patron saint of Florence. The Child is holding a pomegranate, the fruit of Paradise, whose ruby red pips may also symbolise the Passion of Christ.

5

SANDRO BOTTICELLI
Pallas and the Centaur

This painting, owned by Lorenzo di Pierfrancesco de' Medici, originally formed part, along with the *Primavera*, of the furnishings of a room in his palace on Via Larga. Framed in the scenario of an aquatic landscape, standing beside a rocky outcrop, a young woman grasps a lock of hair on the head of a centaur, who appears surprised. Armed with a lance, she is wearing a transparent robe decorated with olive branches and embroidered with a coat-of-arms consisting of three interwoven diamond rings: *Deo amante*, "devoted to God", the emblem first of Cosimo the Elder and then of other members of the Medici family. Enigmatic, clearly symbolical, the painting has a meaning. It is probably an allegory playing on the contrast between two natures, variously interpreted as Chastity and Lust, Humility and Pride, or Instinct and Reason.

SANDRO BOTTICELLI
The birth of Venus

The painting, whose origins and patron are unknown, was by the mid-16th century to be found together with the *Primavera* in the villa at Castello, the former property of Lorenzo di Pierfrancesco de' Medici, who died in 1503.

The title which made the painting famous comes from the last century, and is based on a faulty interpretation of the subject as *Venus Anadiomene* ("arising from the sea"), a subject which the painter Apelles made famous in antiquity. In fact, Sandro Botticelli, inspired by the writings of Homer and Virgil and perhaps by the verses of his friend Poliziano, is narrating a different episode from the legend of the Goddess: her arrival at the island of Kythera or perhaps Cyprus. Against a seascape rendered with the utmost mastery, Venus stands naked on a huge shell, being pushed towards shore by the swell of the sea, helped by the breath of the winds Zephyrus and Aura who embrace softly whilst roses fall from the sky. She is welcomed by a girl wearing a silken cloak embroidered with daisies and other flowers, probably one of Hora or one of the Three Graces. Whilst the figures on the left may be taken from the famous *Tazza Farnese*, now in the Archaeological Museum in Naples but then in the gem collection of Lorenzo the Magnificent, the pose of the main figure is inspired by the antique sculptural type, the *Chaste Venus*, well-known since Medieval times. Like the *Primavera*, this famous work is representative of the most serene and graceful phase of Botticelli's art, linked to the neo-Platonic atmosphere of Lorenzo's age: once again we are shown the fusion of Spirit and Matter, the harmonious marriage of Idea and Nature. Instead of the brilliant and solid colours used for the *Primavera*, it is painted with a mixture of diluted yolk and light tempera which give it an appearance similar to that of a fresco.

7

SANDRO BOTTICELLI
Madonna of the Pomegranate

Around 1487, after having painted the *Madonna of the Magnificat*, Botticelli executed another tondo with the Virgin, six angels and the Christ Child holding a pomegranate. The maturity reached by the artist is evident in the balanced colours of the highly refined garments, and in the harmonious combining of symbolic elements alluding to Mary's purity and grace: lilies, roses, and the words of the Annunciation (AVE GRAZIA PLENA) on the stole worn by the angel at the left. The splendid original frame bears witness to the superb skill of the Florentine woodworkers of that time. The intaglio work with gilded lilies on a blue field, alluding to the alliance between Florence and France, are similar to the ones on the ceiling of the Audience Hall of the Massai di Camera in Palazzo Vecchio, and it is probable that the tondo comes from this hall.

8

SANDRO BOTTICELLI
Calumny

Commissioned by the banker Antonio Segni, this allegory was inspired by the work which Apelles, the mythical painter of antiquity, is said to have painted to refute the calumny spoken against him to King Ptolemy Filelfo by a rival. In this painting the victim of the calumny is dragged before King Midas who is flanked by Suspicion and Ignorance. To the left stands Truth, naked as tradition, next to Repentance.

9

SANDRO BOTTICELLI
Primavera (Spring)

This famous painting was in 1498 in the Via Larga house of Lorenzo and Giovanni di Pierfrancesco de' Medici, the cousins of Lorenzo the Magnificent. Like *Pallas and the Centaur*, the panel hung over the back of a day-bed or chest. By the mid-sixteenth century it hung instead in the Medici villa at Castello, where Vasari described it as "Venus as a symbol of spring, being adorned with flowers by the Graces". The complex allegory seems to have been inspired by the classical texts of Ovid and Lucretius, and by certain verses of Agnolo Poliziano (1475), friend of the Medici and of the artist, who describes a garden with the Three Graces garlanded with flowers and the springtime wind Zephyrus chasing after Flora. The winged genie on the right of the painting is indeed generally thought to be Zephyrus who chased and possessed the nymph Chloris, and then married her, giving her the ability to germinate flowers (here she has blooms falling from her mouth). Near to Chloris is the smiling figure clothed in flowers, fixed forever in the collective imagination, representing the transformation of Chloris into Flora, the Latin goddess of Spring; the woman in the centre is possibly Venus, and this is her garden. The three women on the left entwined in a dance, derived from ancient images of the Three Graces, may be the symbol of Liberality. Above is Cupid, the blindfolded God of love. Finally, the youth with a traveller's hat, sword and winged sandals is certainly Mercury, herald of Jove, who is perhaps here as an emblem of knowledge. The allegory of Spring, the season in which the invisible world of Form descends to mould and shape Matter, may perhaps be celebrating the marriage of the erudite Lorenzo di Pierfrancesco de' Medici, friend of Botticelli, and Semiramide Appiani, a female relative of Simonetta Vespucci, famous for her beauty and for her presumed liaison with Giuliano de' Medici. A more recent interpretation, however, sees the painting as a metaphorical celebration of the Liberal Arts, to be read in a nuptial key. The work is representative of the Golden Age of Lorenzo the Magnificent.

10

SANDRO BOTTICELLI
Adoration of the Magi

Painted for the chapel of Guasparre Lami (agent of the Bankers Guild whose members included the Medici), in the church of Santa Maria Novella, this altarpiece is a public homage to Lorenzo the Magnificent and his family, with whom Botticelli was in contact. Against a backdrop of ancient ruins a favourite scene of the Medici is shown – the procession through the streets in which they took part every year with the Confraternity of Magi, dressed as oriental kings, in commemoration of the sacred event. The painting is rich in portraits of personages well known to the Florentines of the times. Apart from the self-portrait of Botticelli which stares at the viewer from the right of the painting, Giuliano de' Medici stands out on the left; leaning on him is the poet Poliziano with the erudite Pico della Mirandola beside him.

The Magus kneeling at the feet of Jesus is Cosimo the Elder, whilst the king with the red cloak seen from behind is Piero the Gouty, the father of Lorenzo the Magnificent (seen in profile on the right, with a short black garment).

11

SANDRO BOTTICELLI
Portrait of a Youth with a medal

Previously owned by Cardinal Carlo de' Medici, this painting was transferred to the Gallery in 1666. An enigmatic youth stares out at the spectator from a Flemish-style landscape. The medal, coined in 1464, showing the profile of Cosimo the Elder *Pater Patriae* with the inscription MAGNUS COSMUS MEDICES PPP, supports the theory that the sitter was either linked to the Medici circle or was Antonio Filipepi, goldsmith and medallist, brother of the artist.

79

SANDRO BOTTICELLI
St. Ambrose Altarpiece
(or of the Converted Sisters)

This work was transferred to the Gallery of the Accademia in 1808 from the Benedictine monastery of St. Ambrose, and it was originally thought that the work had been there since its completion. However, neither St. Ambrose nor any of the Benedictine patron saints are portrayed, but instead Cosmas and Damian, saints traditionally linked with the Medici, who kneel at the feet of the Madonna; also are Mary Magdalen, John the Baptist, St. Francis and Saint Catherine of Alexandria. The presence of St. Francis of Assisi suggests that this might be the Botticelli panel seen in the 16th century by Vasari in the church of San Francesco in Montevarchi, but this hypotheses has yet to be confirmed.

However, the theory that the altarpiece originated in the convent of the Converted Sisters, which for a long time gave its name to the painting, has now been refuted. Now that many layers of overpainting have been removed by delicate restoration, the original style of the work has re-emerged, to make it a definite attribution and the first known altarpiece by this artist. The composition and the pictorial *ductus* now show clear evidence of the influence of Filippo Lippi, whose pupil Botticelli was in Prato until the monk left for Spoleto in 1467. The influence of Verrocchio can also be seen in the almost metallic quality of the garments; he became Sandro Botticelli's master in that same year.

14

HUGO VAN DER GOES
The Portinari Triptych

The triptych was painted in Bruges for Tommaso Portinari, an agent of the Medici and councillor of the Duchy of Burgundy. Portinari was in Flanders from 1455 and in 1470 married Maria Maddalena Baroncelli, by whom he was to have ten children. In this triptych the spouses are portrayed on the side panels, absorbed in prayer before the *Adoration of the shepherds*, with patron saints and the three eldest children, Maria Margherita, Antonio and Pigello (born in 1474, the year from which the probable date of the painting is calculated). The work was sent to Florence by the owners in 1483, destined for the main altar of the church of Sant'Egidio, their favourite church. The great Flemish triptych with its minute natural details made a significant impact on the artists then working in Florence.

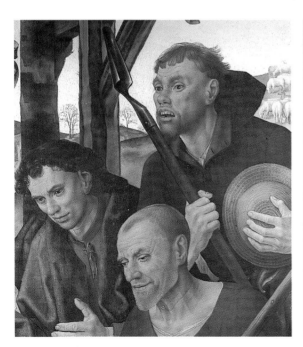

16

DOMENICO GHIRLANDAIO
*Madonna enthroned
with Angels and Saints*

Originally on the altar of San Giusto degli Inge-suati, the painting was transferred to San Giovanni Battista della Calza where it was seen by Vasari. Against the background of a crystal clear sky, a balustrade covered in jewels supports the enthroned Virgin, surrounded by four garlanded angel. The Child is blessing St. Justus, the patron saint of the church, who kneels at the front of the painting. The other figures are archangels Michael and Raphael, standing, and St. Zanobius, patron saint of Florence, kneeling on the right. Standing out against the landscape are cypresses, a hibiscus and an orange tree. Vasari praised the metallic brilliance of the archangel Michael's armour, obtained not through the application of gold, but with pure colour, an innovation introduced by this artist. Ghirlandaio, also a fine portraitist, was one of the main artists to take an interest in Flemish art, the influences of which can be seen in his landscapes and decorative details.

18

SANDRO BOTTICELLI
*San Marco Altarpiece
(Coronation of the Virgin)*

Commissioned in 1488 by the Goldsmiths Guild for the chapel of their patron St. Eligio in San Marco. After a long restoration the great altarpiece is now considered a key work of Botticelli's mature period. The composition is very new for its time, being clearly divided into two zones: in the upper part, against a burst of golden rays, is the scene of the Virgin crowned by God the Fa-

ther, surrounded by dancing angels; below are the saints John the Evangelist, Augustine and Jerome, whose writings allude to the episode depicted above, and on the extreme right is St. Eligio. A deep sense of spirituality emanates from the painting, prefiguring later, still more mystical works such as *Calumny*. The predella, divided by small painted columns, announces the themes of the altarpiece; among the stories of the saints is that of Eligio, who was also patron saint of blacksmiths, tricking a demon by shoeing the detached leg of a horse.

Room 15 ❖ Leonardo

This room was restructured and the display reorganized in 1991. The works, lit from above by a wide skylight, bear witness above all to the early phases of Leonardo's Florentine activity, from his beginnings in Verrocchio's studio to his departure for Milan in 1482. Also exhibited here are some recently restored panel paintings by Signorelli, by the graceful Perugino, an Umbrian artist who was active in Florence at the end of the century, as well some works by the "eccentric" Piero di Cosimo, whose compositions were unusually inventive. The works of these three artists form an ideal link with other paintings carried out in Florence between the 15th and 16th centuries now on display in Room 19 (beyond the Tribune) and Room 25 (west wing).

The works

1. LUCA SIGNORELLI
*Crucifixion
with Mary Magdalene*
Early 16th century
Tempera on canvas
247x165
Inv. 1890 no. 8368
Restored: 1989

2. LUCA SIGNORELLI
*The Trinity,
the Madonna
and two Saints*
c. 1500-1510
Oil on wood "curved"
272x180
Inv. 1890 no. 8369
Restored: 2000

3. PERUGINO
Agony in the garden
c. 1492
Oil on wood
166x171
Inv. 1890 no. 8367
Restored: 1998

4. PERUGINO
*Crucifixion
with Saints*
1492
Oil on wood
203x108
Inv. 1890 no. 3254
Restored: 1998

5. PERUGINO
Pietà
c. 1493-1494
Grease tempera on wood
168x176
Inv. 1890 no. 8365
Restored: 1984

6. LEONARDO DA VINCI
Annunciation
c. 1475-1480
Tempera mixed
with oil on wood
98x217
Inv. 1890 no. 1618
Restored: 2000

7. LEONARDO DA VINCI
Adoration of the Magi
1481
Tempera mixed
with oil on wood; 243x246
Inv. 1890 no. 1594

**8. VERROCCHIO
AND LEONARDO DA VINCI**
Baptism of Christ
Variously dated from 1473 to c. 1478
Tempera and oil on wood
180x152
Inv. 1890 no. 8358
Restored: 1998

9. PERUGINO
*Madonna and Child
enthroned with Saints*
Signed and dated 1493
Grease tempera on wood
178x164
Inv. 1890 no. 1435. Restored: 1995

10. LORENZO DI CREDI
Adoration of the shepherds
Before 1510
Oil on wood
224x196
Inv. 1890 no. 8399

11. PIERO DI COSIMO
Incarnation of Christ
c. 1498-1505
Oil on wood
206x172
Inv. 1890 no. 506
Restored: 1980

5

PERUGINO
Pietà

This work, like the *Agony in the garden*, was painted by Perugino for the screen wall in the Inge-suati church outside the Pinti Gate. The panel painting was transferred many times after the destruction of the convent in 1529. In an atmosphere of deep spirituality, perhaps influenced by the sermons of Savonarola, the Madonna supports across her knees the rigid and ashen body of Christ. He is also supported by the kneeling John the Evangelist, and by Mary Magdalen who is seated in prayer. Standing like statues, Nicodemus and Joseph of Arimathea serve as a link between the holy scene and the airy architectural structure.

LEONARDO DA VINCI
Annunciation

New hypotheses for the reading of this painting have been stimulated by its restoration, completed in March 2000, which has revealed not only its luminosity and clarity of detail but a stronger sense of perspective in the architectural foreshortening on the right (the door, of which both doorjambs can now be seen, gives a clearer glimpse of the baldachin in the room). Still controversial is the dating of the work painted in Florence for the Church of San Bartolomeo a Oliveto. Hypotheses range from the early 1460s, when the artist was only a little over twenty, almost up to the beginning of the next decade.

In some details the influence of Verrocchio, or perhaps Leonardo's homage to his master, can be recognized (especially in the base supporting the lectern, reminiscent of the Sepulcher of Giovanni and Piero de' Medici in San Lorenzo). The Virgin's arm seems disproportionately elongated, unable to reach the book on the lectern, and the angel's shadow is too dark for the light of dawn, which restoration has shown to be the hour chosen by Leonardo as the setting, perhaps with symbolic overtones, for the Annunciation. The meadow is sprinkled with a myriad of flowers studied from life; in the beautiful landscape, typical Tuscan cypresses trail off into the distance where the minute details of a lake-side city blend into the bluish tones of the bare mountains in the background.

7

LEONARDO DA VINCI
Adoration of the Magi

This was transferred from the collection of Antonio and Giulio de' Medici to the Gallery in 1670 and later to Castello, to return to the Uffizi in 1794. The work was commissioned from Leonardo by the Augustinian monks of San Donato a Scopeto in 1481, but remained unfinished at the time of the artist's departure to Milan, one year later. To substitute it, the monks asked Filippino Lippi to make a similar panel painting (Room 8). Because of the varnishes added during the centuries, the panel painting by Leonardo, which has remained in a monochrome state, is almost illegible. From recent research done on a preparatory drawing a complex perspective system can be worked out. The magnificent setting is made up of several narrative episodes brought together by a kind of continuous motion; the scene filled with people and animals was meant to give the illusion of a figurative metamorphosis rich in symbolic meanings. The ruins in the background may allude to the fall of paganism at the advent of Christ.

8

VERROCCHIO AND LEONARDO DA VINCI
Baptisme of Christ

This newly restored panel painting came from the church of San Michele in San Salvi and confirms the vitality of Verrocchio's workshop which was amongst the most famous in Renaissance Florence. According to Vasari, Verrocchio gave up painting because his pupil Leonardo had surpassed him. Although Leonardo's hand has now been identified in the angel on the left and the background landscape, interventions by other artists are visible in this painting. The dry style of the palm tree and rocky outcrop behind John the Baptist's shoulders is very different from the mountains fading softly into the watery landscape beyond the heads of the angels. Christ and John the Baptist are also treated in different styles, the former smoothly finished, the latter harsh and tense. It is assumed that another important artist worked on this painting (the angel on the right has even been attributed to Botticelli), assisted by apprentices.

Room 16 ❖ Geographical Maps

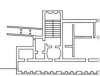
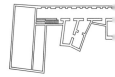

At the time of Francesco I, this room appeared as a terrace open towards the East, with two windows on another wall (later closed up) beside a fresco showing the island of Elba. Around 1589 the new Grand Duke Ferdinand ordered a glass window to close the loggia, which was then frescoed by Ludovico Buti with geographical descriptions of Tuscany, following scientific surveys of the territory, drawn by the cartographer Stefano Bonsignori. In the enthusiasm for scientific progress, which had already been shown by the Duke's father Cosimo for reasons which included political prestige, the room was set aside to house outstanding scientific instruments, such as the large wooden armillary sphere made by Antonio Santucci delle Pomarance (1593), the globe attributed to Ignazio Danti, and Galileo's telescope and astrolabe. Still undergoing reorganization at present the room contained copies of the original scientific instruments which were transferred some time ago to the Florence Museum of the History of Science. The ceiling is decorated with Mythological canvases by Jacopo Zucchi, who painted them in Rome for Ferdinando de' Medici, who was then a Cardinal (c. 1572). They were later inserted between the beams which were decorated with garlands of fruit and flowers by Ludovico Buti.

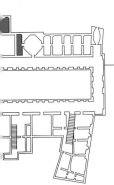

Room 17 ❖ Hermaphrodite

This delightful little room, joined to the Tribune, dates back to the time of Ferdinando I, when it was called "The Mathematics Room". Today it takes the name of the Sleeping Hermaphrodite, *a sculpture from antiquity famous for its ambiguous sensuality, which has been on display here since 1669. The work, many variations of which exist in other museums, is a copy in Parian marble from the bronze original of Polykles and was acquired by Ferdinando II from the Ludovisi Collection in Rome. The inspiration for the room and its decorations came from Filippo Pigafetta, following his passion for geometry and mechanics. Around the year 1598, he suggested building a room devoted to "the study of military architecture", with a display of mechanical instruments, weight-lifting machines, "books, geographical maps and plans, and models of fortresses". Certain frescoes on the first ceiling (painted by Giulio Parigi, a painter, architect, and Medicean engineer), hint at the ambitions of the Grand Duke for expansion into foreign territories and nautical exploits. Others attest to the hydraulic skills of Tuscan technicians and the mathematical competence of his men-at-arms, with a celebration of the greatest historical figures in this field: Pythagorus, Ptolemy and Archimedes, the latter portrayed during the siege of Syracuse.*

Room 18 ❖ Tribune

The octagonal Tribune, planned by Buontalenti in 1584, with its cupola encrusted with moth-er-of-pearl shells set into a background of scarlet lacquer is the jewel in the Gallery's crown. Through windows made from Oriental crystal, natural light falls softly upon the paintings, on the walls covered in red velvet, on the sculptures and precious objects. The skirting board, now lost, painted by Jacopo Ligozzi, had a frieze with fish, birds, streams and plants. The room symbolises the cosmos and its elements: the lantern with its wind rose represents air; the shells, water; the red walls, fire; the marble and the semi-precious stones of the pavement, earth. In the centre, the octagonal jewel case (lost) encrusted with gold, gems, and rare stones, and with boxes decorated by Giambologna, echoed the shape of the room. Over the centuries the layout of the room has been rearranged many times, but the ancient sculptures are still here, pride of the Tribune since the 17th century, as is the table with its mosaic of semi-precious stones from the Opificio of the Grand Duke (1633-1649), and finally many paintings from 16th century Flo-rence. The date 1601, found on the cupola, indicates the year when the room was completed.

The works

The paintings

1. **ALESSANDRO ALLORI** (below)
Portrait of Bianca Cappello
c. 1580
Fresco
75x52
Inv. 1890 no. 1500

2. **AGNOLO BRONZINO** (above)
Annunciation
c. 1550
Tempera on wood
57x43.5
Inv. 1890 no. 1547

3. **GIORGIO VASARI**
Portrait of Lorenzo the Magnificent
1534
Tempera on wood
90x72
Inv. 1890 no. 1578

4. **DANIELE DA VOLTERRA**
(below)
Massacre of the Innocents
1557
Tempera on wood
51x42
Inv. 1890 no. 1429

5. **CARLETTO** (above)
Creation of Eve
c. 1586
Oil on canvas
96x115
Inv. 1890 no. 954

6. **PONTORMO**
Portrait of Cosimo the Elder
c. 1519-1520
Oil on wood
86x65
Inv. 1890 no. 3574

7. **PONTORMO** (below)
Madonna and Child with the infant St. John
c. 1527-1528
Tempera on wood
89x74
Inv. 1890 no. 4347
Restored: 1996

8. **PONTORMO** (above)
Adam and Eve
c. 1519-1520
Oil on wood
45x31
Inv. 1890 no. 1517

9. **AGNOLO BRONZINO** (below)
Portrait of Girl with book
c. 1545
Tempera on wood
58x46.5
Inv. 1890 no. 770

10. **RIDOLFO DEL GHIRLANDAIO** (above)
Portrait of a Youth
c. 1517-1520
Tempera on wood
43x53.5
Inv. 1890 no. 2155

11. **AGNOLO BRONZINO**
Portrait of Lucrezia Panciatichi
c. 1541
Tempera on wood
104x84
Inv. 1890 no. 736

12. **CECCHINO SALVIATI** (below)
Charity
c. 1543-1545
Oil on wood
156x122
Inv. 1890 no. 2157
Restored: 2002

13. **CARLETTO** (above)
The Original Sin
c. 1586
Oil on canvas
98x113
Inv. 1890 no. 960

14. **AGNOLO BRONZINO**
Portrait of Bartolomeo Panciatichi
c. 1541
Tempera on wood
104x84
Inv. 1890 no. 741

15. **CECCHINO SALVIATI** (below)
Christ bearing the Cross
c. 1540-1545
Tempera on wood
66x45
Inv. 1890 no. 801

16. **AGNOLO BRONZINO** (above)
Portrait of Maria de' Medici
1551
Oil on wood
52.5x38
Inv. 1890 no. 1572

17. **AGNOLO BRONZINO** (below)
Portrait of Francesco I de' Medici as a Young man
1551
Tempera on wood
58.5x41.5
Inv. 1890 no. 1571

18. **PONTORMO** (above)
Leda and the Swan
c. 1512-1513
Tempera on wood
55x40
Inv. 1890 no. 1556

19. **FRANCIABIGIO**
Madonna of the Well
c. 1517-1518
Tempera on wood
106x81
Inv. 1890 no. 1445

20. **RAPHAEL AND ASSISTANCE** (below)
St. John in the desert
c. 1519-1520
Oil on canvas
165x147
Inv. 1890 no. 1446

21. **CARLETTO** (above)
Expulsion from Paradise
c. 1586
Oil on canvas
99x110
Inv. 1890 no. 944

22. **GIULIO ROMANO**
Madonna and Child
c. 1520-1530
Tempera on wood
105x77
Inv. 1890 no. 2147

23. **AGNOLO BRONZINO** (below)
Portrait of Giovanni de' Medici as a child
1545
Tempera on wood
58x45.6
Inv. 1890 no. 1475

24. **ROSSO FIORENTINO** (above)
Musical Cherub
1521
Oil on wood
47x39
Inv. 1890 no. 1505
Restored: 2000

25. **AGNOLO BRONZINO**
Portrait of Bia de' Medici
c. 1542
Tempera on wood
63x48
Inv. 1890 no. 1472

26. **GIORGIO VASARI**
The Prophet Elisha
c. 1566
Tempera on wood
40x29
Inv. 1890 no. 1470

27. **AGNOLO BRONZINO**
Portrait of Young man with a lute
c. 1532-1540
Tempera on wood
98x82.5
Inv. 1890 no. 1575

28. **AGNOLO BRONZINO** (below)
Eleonora di Toledo with her son Giovanni
c. 1545
Oil on wood
115x96
Inv. 1890 no. 748

29. **CARLETTO** (above)
The family of Adam
c. 1586
Oil on canvas
99x111
Inv. 1890 no. 951

30. **ANDREA DEL SARTO**
Woman with the "Petrarchino"
c. 1528
Oil on wood
87x69
Inv. 1890 no. 783
Restored: 1986

31. **AGNOLO BRONZINO** (below)
Portrait of Cosimo I in armor
c. 1545
Tempera on wood
71x57
Dep. inv. no. 28

32. **GIORGIO VASARI** (above)
Allegory of the Immaculate Conception
1541
Oil on wood
58x39
Inv. 1890 no. 1524

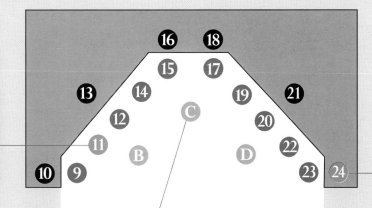

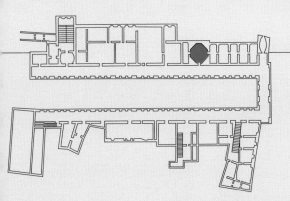

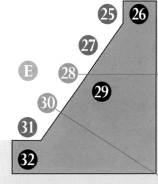

The statues

A. *Satyr with Kroupézion*
Copy of a bronze
original, 2nd century BC
(modern head)
Greek marble
Height 1.43
Inv. 1914 no. 220

B. *Wrestlers*
Copy, second half
of the 3rd century BC
of a Hellenistic
bronze original
Greek marble
Height 0.89
Width 0.90
Inv. 1914 no. 216

C. *Medici Venus*
Copy from an Greek
original of the 2nd century BC
Greek marble
Height 1.53
Inv. 1914 no. 224

D. *Scythian flayer
of Marsyas
(the Knife-grinder)*
Copy of a Greek
original of the Pergamum
school, 3rd century BC
Asian marble
Height 1.05
Inv. 1914 no. 230

E. *Apollino*
Copy of an original
of the *Apollo Lykeios* type
by Praxiteles,
4th century BC
Marble
w. m.
Inv. 1914 no. 229

C *Medici Venus*

The *Medici Venus*, one of the most celebrated classical sculptures of the granducal collection, was acquired in the early 17th century for the family's Roman villa on the Pincio, and was then transferred in 1677 from Villa Medici to the Uffizi by Cosimo III. Despite the reputation of the Grand Duke as a bigot, this sculpture with its disturbing beauty (a type already known in Rome since at least the 12th century) took place of honour in the Tribune and soon became the focus of unrestrained admiration.

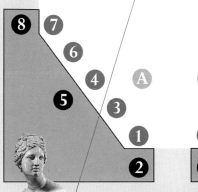

93

AGNOLO BRONZINO
Lucrezia Panciatichi

Lying against Lucrezia's sumptuous dress, the gold and enamel plaques of her necklace carry the words, "AMOUR DURE SANS FIN", which attracted the fantasy of writers such as Henry James and Vernon Lee. The book in her right hand is a *Book of*

Daily Offices, with prayers dedicated to Mary. This intense portrait shows Lucrezia Pucci, wife of Bartolomeo Panciatichi, who was a Florentine academician from 1541. Panciatichi himself had his portrait done by Bronzino, who also painted a *Holy Family* for him (Room 27). Both the portraits, now in the Tribune, were in 1584 still to be found in the house of his son Carlo, a servant of Francesco I.

ROSSO FIORENTINO
Musical Cherub

This work was long believed to be a complete panel painting, but recent research using reflectography suggests that it is probably the fragment of an altarpiece with the Virgin and Saints, of which there remains no other trace. The cherub probably sat on steps, indicated by parallel incisions on the surface of the painting. Down towards the right the signature (partially rubbed off) became legible, as did the date, perhaps painted by Rosso himself on the already sepa-

rate fragment of the panel. It is possible that it was painted far from Florence, as the artist mentions his origin alongside his signature, declaring himself to be "florent[inus]". The development of this artist, whose mode of expression was unique in the art world of his time, often crossed over with that of artists who were strangers or "eccentrics", thanks to his many journeys to other Italian cities, and his final destination at the Fontainebleau court of King François I in France.

28

AGNOLO BRONZINO
Eleonora di Toledo with her son Giovanni

Eleonora di Toledo, wife of Cosimo I de' Medici from 1539, is shown here with her second son. Her highly-valued role as a mother is marked by the pomegranate on her clothing. This symbol of fertility is also present on the vault of her chapel in Palazzo Vecchio, also frescoed by Bronzino, prolific portraitist to the Medici court.

The brocade dress with Spanish embroidery is identical to the one found in 1857 inside the tomb of the Duchess in the Medici Chapel. The background landscape may show the Grand Duke's dominions.

30

ANDREA DEL SARTO
Woman with the "Petrarchino"

This young woman, elegantly dressed and adorned with a magnificent jeweled pendant, is smiling mysteriously, perhaps to her beloved, while pointing in her book, the famous "Petrarchino" which appears in many other portraits of the time, to the verses of two love sonnets by Petrarca, the fourteenth century poet: "Ite caldi sospiri al freddo core" ("Go, warm sighs, to the cold heart", CLIII), and "Le stelle, il cielo et gli elementi a prova" ("The stars, the sky and the elements compete", CLIV). This is probably a portrait of Maria del Berrettaio, born in 1513 from del Sarto's first marriage to his adored wife Lucrezia.

Room 19 ❖ Perugino and Signorelli

This room contains masterpieces by artists, not Florentine alone, who exemplify the crucial moment of transition from late 15th century painting to that of the first decades of the 16th century. There are portraits of extraordinary intensity, painted with almost photographic precision, such as the magnificent ones by Perugino, who worked for years in Florence, and works of serene equilibrium, like the Annunciation *by Lorenzo di Credi, one of Verrocchio's pupils. Of special interest are the two tondoes by Luca Signorelli (Inv. nos. 1605, 502), the artist from Cortona highly sensitive to the fascination of antiquity, who worked not only in Florence but also in Rome, Orvieto and other Italian cities on major projects including frescoes. An ideal conclusion to this itinerary is provided by the allegory of the myth of Perseus painted by the eccentric Piero di Cosimo, an enigmatic work whose dating is still controversial.*

The works

1. MARCO PALMEZZANO
Crucifixion
c. 1500-1510
Tempera on wood
112x90
Inv. 1890 no. 1418

2. LORENZO DI ALESSANDRO DA SAN SEVERINO
Pietà
c. 1491
Tempera on wood; 62x158
Inv. 1890 no. 3142

3. LORENZO DI CREDI
Annunciation
c. 1480-1485
Oil on wood; 88x71
Inv. 1890 no. 1597

4. LORENZO DI CREDI
Venus
c. 1490
Tempera on wood
151x69
Inv. 1890 no. 3094
Restored: 2000

5. PIERO DI COSIMO
Liberation of Andromeda
Variously dated 1510 or 1513
Oil on wood; 70x123
Inv. 1890 no. 1536

6. LUCA SIGNORELLI
Holy Family
c. 1484-1490
Oil on wood; diam. 124
Inv. 1890 no. 1605
Restored: 2000

7. LUCA SIGNORELLI
Allegory of Fecundity and Abundance
Early 16th century
Oil on wood; 58x105.5
Inv. 1890 no. 3107
Restored: 2001

8. PERUGINO
Portrait of Francesco delle Opere
1494
Tempera on wood
52x44
Inv. 1890 no. 1700

9. LUCA SIGNORELLI
Madonna and Child
c. 1490-1495
Tempera on wood
170x117.5
Inv. 1890 no. 502
Restored: 2002

10. PERUGINO (below)
Portraits of Don Biagio Milanesi and Baldassare Vallombrosano
1500
Tempera on wood
28.5x26.5 and 26x27
Inv. 1890 nos. 8375, 8376
Restored: 1998

11. PERUGINO (above)
Portrait of a Young man
c. 1494
Oil on wood; 37x26
Inv. 1890 no. 1474

12. LORENZO COSTA
St. Sebastian
c. 1490-1491
Tempera on wood
55x49
Inv. 1890 no. 3282

13. GIROLAMO GENGA
Martyrdom of St. Sebastian
Early 16th century
Tempera on wood
100x83
Inv. 1890 no. 1535

14. FRANCIA
Portrait of Evangelista Scappi
c. 1500-1503
Tempera on wood
55x44
Inv. 1890 no. 1444

5

PIERO DI COSIMO
Liberation of Andromeda

Initially exhibited in the Tribune as a work in which Piero di Cosimo was following a drawing by Leonardo, this is now the artist's most famous painting precisely for its completely original composition. It narrates in great detail the myth of Perseus liberating Andromeda by killing the sea monster. The central scene is dominated by the dragon in its death-throes, but the eye is also drawn to the fascinating, almost grotesque landscape, and to the detail in the painting – from the exotic turbaned figures at the far edges of the painting to the nordic wood and straw huts on the unlikely-looking hilltops in the back-ground. The musical instruments are equally unlikely: they could never be played as they are all missing a sound box or strings. It has been suggested that the scene in this painting was inspired by the Florentine carnival of 1513 when the Medici returned to the city – symbolised by the dried branch with its new shoot, the Medici "broncone" emblem.

A recent study (L. Cavazzini, 1997) suggests that the work, which according to Vasari was painted for one of the Strozzi family, belonged to Filippo the Younger, who in 1510 paid Piero for a "work" for his bedchamber.

8

PERUGINO
Portrait of Francesco delle Opere

This wonderful portrait is very probably of Francesco delle Opere, as indicated on the rear of the painting. This Florentine artisan, who died in Venice in 1516, was the brother of a friend of the painter, Giovanni delle Corniole, a master gem cutter. The "photographic" precision of the features, the position of the figure with its hand leaning on the balustrade, and the landscape in the background, are clearly inspired by Flemish art, particularly by Memling's portraits which were already known in Florence (Room 22).

Room 20 ❖ Dürer

As in the previous room and the four that follow, the original fresco decoration was carried out in 1588 by Ludovico Buti. The four views of Florentine spectacles on the vault were however repainted during the middle of the 19th century. Under the current layout, the room houses masterpieces from the great German painters, Dürer and Cranach, and the Flemish painter Bruegel the Elder. Amongst the works of Dürer (who made two key trips to Italy in 1494 and 1505), the Portrait of the artist's father *(1490) and the* Madonna with Pear *(1526) stand out, along with the* Adoration *discussed below.*

The works

1. LUKAS CRANACH THE ELDER
*Madonna and Child
with the infant St. John the Baptist*
Initialed and dated 1514
Oil on wood; 74x57
Without Inv. no.
Painting stolen by the Certosa
of Galluzzo in 1973 and retrieved
on February 28, 2001

**2. GERMAN SCHOOL (ATTR.
HANS SÜSS VON KULMBACH)**
Crucifixion
c. 1511-1514
Oil on wood; 167x92
Inv. 1890 no. 1025

3. LUKAS CRANACH THE YOUNGER
*Portrait of Lukas
Cranach the Elder*
1550
Oil on wood; 64x49
Inv. 1890 no. 1631

4. LUKAS CRANACH THE ELDER
*Portraits of Martin Luther
and his wife Katherina Bore*
Initialed and dated 1529
Oil on wood
36.5x23 and 37x23
Inv. 1890 nos. 1160, 1139
Restored: 1985

**5. WORKSHOP OF LUKAS
CRANACH THE ELDER**
Portrait of a Lady
c. 1550
Oil on wood
42x29
Without Inv. no.

6. HANS MALER ZU SCHWAZ
Portrait of Ferdinand of Hapsburg
1524
Oil on wood; 33x23
Inv. 1890 no. 1215

7. HANS BURGKMAIR THE ELDER
Portrait of a Man
Signed and dated 1506
Parchment on wood
27.2x22.5
Dep. Inv. no. 432

8. LUKAS CRANACH THE ELDER
St. George
Dated 1520 on the horse's tail
Oil on wood
19x18
Inv. 1890 no. 1056

**9. WORKSHOP OF LUKAS
CRANACH THE ELDER**
*Portraits of Frederick III the Wise
and John I, Electors of Saxony*
1533
Oil on wood
20x15 (each)
Inv. 1890 nos. 1149, 1150
Restored: 1994

**10. WORKSHOP OF LUKAS
CRANACH THE ELDER**
*Martin Luther
and Philip Melanchton*
1534
Oil on wood
21x16 (each)
Inv. 1890 nos. 512, 472

11. JOOS VAN CLEVE
Portrait of an Unknown man
c. 1512
Oil on wood
31x20
Inv. 1890 no. 1645
In restoration

12. GERMAN SCHOOL
Open Book
First quarter of the 16th century
Oil on wood
70.2x65
Inv. 1890 no. 6191

13. ALBRECHT DÜRER
*Madonna of the Pear
(Madonna and Child)*
Initialed and dated 1526
Oil on wood; 43x31
Inv. 1890 no. 1171

14. ALBRECHT DÜRER
Portrait of the artist's father
1490
Oil on wood; 47.5x39.5
Inv. 1890 no. 1086

15. ALBRECHT DÜRER
Adoration of the Magi
Initialed and dated 1504
Oil on wood; 99x113.5
Inv. 1890 no. 1434

16. HANS BALDUNG GRIEN (ATTR.)
*Adam
and Eve*
After 1507
Oil on wood
212x85 (each)
Inv. 1890 nos. 8433, 8432

17. ALBRECHT DÜRER
St. Philip the Apostle
Initialed and dated 1516
Tempera on canvas
45x38
Inv. 1890 no. 1089

18. HANS SÜSS VON KULMBACH
Stories of St. Peter and St. Paul
1514-1516
Oil on wood
from 128.5x95.5 to 132x96
Inv. 1890 nos. 1034, 1020, 1060,
1047, 1044, 1072, 1030, 1058

19. ALBRECHT DÜRER
St. James the Apostle
Initialed and dated 1516
Tempera on canvas
46x37
Inv. 1890 no. 1099

20. JAN BRUEGEL THE ELDER
The Great Calvary
(from Dürer)
Signed and dated 1604
Oil on wood
62x42
Inv. 1890 no. 1083

21. LUKAS CRANACH THE ELDER
*Adam
and Eve*
Initialed and dated 1528
on the *Adam* panel
Oil on wood
172x63 e 167x61
Inv. 1890 nos. 1459, 1458
Restored: 1999

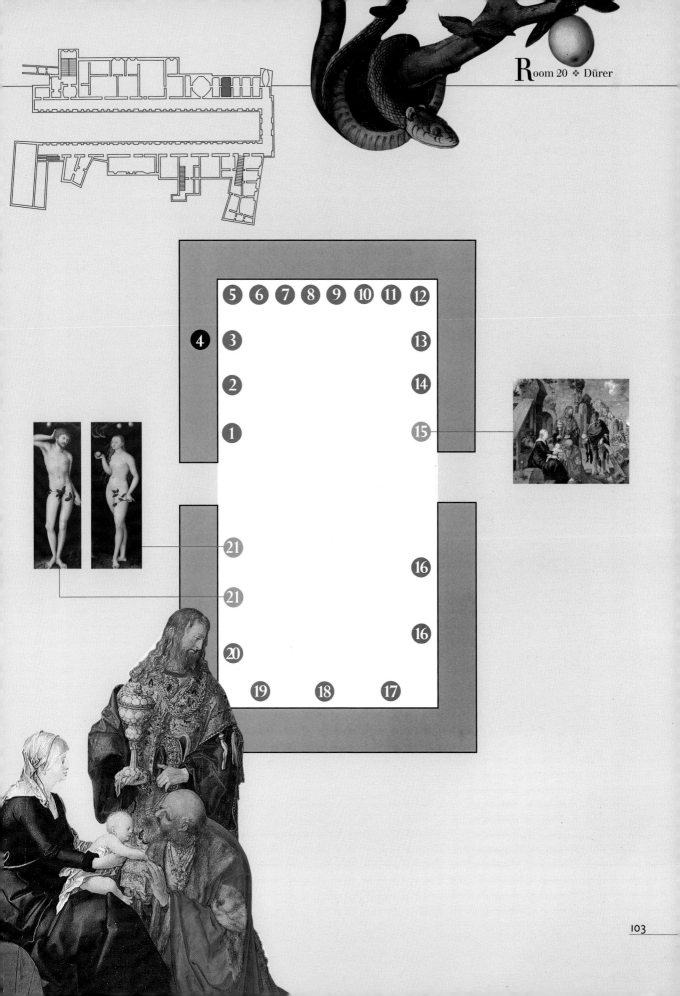

5 6 7 8 9 10 11 12

4 3 13

2 14

1 15

21

16

21

16

20

19 18 17

15

ALBRECHT DÜRER
Adoration of the Magi

Painted in 1504, just before Dürer's second trip to Italy, the intense colors and use of perspective are both reminiscent of Venetian painting, particularly that of Mantegna and Giovanni Bellini. The classical ruins, typical of Italian painting, combine well with the nordic-style landscape with small figures in the distance. The careful study of plants and animals, so rich in symbolism, confirms Dürer's practise of studying nature, characteristic of most of this German master's work.

21

LUKAS CRANACH THE ELDER
Adam
and *Eve*

The typical representation of Adam and Eve depicted before their sin dates back to a famous etching made by Dürer in 1504. Since at least 1510, Lukas Cranach worked with this same subject (*Adam* and *Eve*, Warsaw Museum, 59x44), returning to it in 1528 in these two recently restored panels, documented as existing in the granducal collections in 1688. Here too Adam and Eve have not yet tasted the apple. Their nude bodies, barely covered by small branches from the apple tree, are exhibited with unabashed serenity. In the same room are two paintings of similar subject, attributed to Baldung Grien (Inv. nos. 8433, 8432), a pupil Dürer's in Nuremberg. These figures are copied from Dürer's *Adam* and *Eve* now in the Prado (209x81), painted in 1507.

Room 21 ❖ Giambellino and Giorgione

As in the previous two rooms adjoining the Tribune and the two to follow, this room was part of the space that Ferdinando I dedicated to his collection of armoury in 1588. Ferdinando, who succeeded his brother Francesco as Grand Duke, took great interest in the Gallery and in increasing his collections, amongst which that of weapons and armour is particularly valuable. The frescoes on the ceiling, which Ludovico Buti is principally responsible, represent battles and grotesque motifs showing Indians and tropical fauna and flora, displaying the expansionist tendencies of the Medici towards the New World, and particularly Mexico, from whence many pieces in their collection came, formerly kept in what is now Room 24. Today, Room 21 contains various masterpieces by artists active in the second half of the 15ᵗʰ century and the early 16ᵗʰ century: Venetians such as Giovanni Bellini and Giorgione, and artists from Ferrara such as Cosmè Tura.

The works

1. GIORGIONE AND ASSISTANCE
The judgement of Solomon
c. 1502-1508
Oil on wood
89x72
Inv. 1890 no. 947

**2. VENETIAN PAINTER
(ALSO ATTR. TO GIORGIONE OR TO PAOLO MORANDO KNOWN AS CAVAZZOLA)**
Man in armour with a squire
(the so-called *Gattamelata*)
1510-1515
Oil on canvas
89x72
Inv. 1890 no. 911
Restored: 1990

3. GIORGIONE AND ASSISTANCE
Moses undergoing trial by fire
c. 1502-1505
Oil on wood
89x72
Inv. 1890 no. 945

**4. GIOVANNI BELLINI
KNOWN AS GIAMBELLINO**
Lamentation over the Dead Christ
Late 15ᵗʰ-early 16ᵗʰ century
Tempera on wood
74x118
Inv. 1890 no. 943

**5. GIOVANNI BELLINI
KNOWN AS GIAMBELLINO**
Sacred Allegory
Variously dated from 1487
to 1501
Oil on wood
73x119
Inv. 1890 no. 903

6. COSMÈ TURA
St. Dominic
c. 1475
Tempera on wood
51x32
Inv. 1890 no. 3273

**7. GIOVANNI BELLINI
KNOWN AS GIAMBELLINO**
Portrait of a Gentlemen
Late 15ᵗʰ-early 16ᵗʰ century
Oil on wood
31x26
Inv. 1890 no. 1863

8. CIMA DA CONEGLIANO
Madonna and Child
c. 1504
Tempera on wood
66x57
Inv. 1890 no. 902

9. VITTORE CARPACCIO (ATTR.)
Prophet (or *Classical Allegory*)
Early 16ᵗʰ century
Oil on canvas
186x87
Inv. 1890 no. 9939
Work acquired
by Rodolfo Siviero

10. VITTORE CARPACCIO (ATTR.)
Sibyl (or *Classical Allegory*)
Early 16ᵗʰ century
Oil on canvas
186x87
Inv. 1890 no. 9938
Work acquired
by Rodolfo Siviero

11. BARTOLOMEO VIVARINI
St. Ludovic of Toulouse
c. 1465
Tempera on wood
68x36
Inv. 1890 no. 3346

12. LORENZO COSTA
Portrait of Giovanni Bentivoglio
c. 1490-1501
Tempera on wood
55x49
Inv. 1890 no. 8384

13. VITTORE CARPACCIO
Halberdiers and Old men
Variously dated from 1493 to 1505
Oil on wood
68x42
Inv. 1890 no. 901

GIORGIONE AND ASSISTANCE
Moses undergoing trial by fire

Like the *pendant* with *The judgement of Solomon*, this small panel painting was listed in 1692 as part of the patrimony of the Grand Duchess of Tuscany at Poggio Imperiale. Moses is repre-sented here as a newborn baby, whom Pharaoh, sitting on his throne, is subjecting to trial by burn-ing coals in order to verify why the baby had tak-en the crown from his head. This rare episode is narrated in Jewish medieval texts such as the *Shemot Rabbà* which recount legends and moral teachings on Biblical figures and events.

GIOVANNI BELLINI KNOW AS GIAMBELLINO
Sacred Allegory

Many different theories have been advanced concerning the symbolic meaning of this enig-matic *Allegory* painted by Giovanni Bellini. The painting is full of saints and animals including a centaur, set in a peaceful, aquatic landscape, rich in interesting detail to be noted and ex-plored. Defined as "unique and disturbingly in-explicable", it is difficult to date precisely over the long development of Bellini's career. On the terrace, a kind of *hortus conclusus* or sacred en-closure, the Virgin is flanked by two women. She is the only one seated with the exception of the Infant Jesus to whom a child (perhaps the infant St. John) offers a fallen apple from a small tree (perhaps the Tree of Life) being shaken by another child in the centre of the composition, which is dominated by a chequered pavement in a design which may allude to the Cross. To the right are two saints, Jerome (or Job) and Se-bastian. At the balustrade is St. Paul driving away an Asian man (a heretic?) with his sword, and St. Peter (or St. Joseph). On the opposite side of the bank, to the right, is St. Anthony's hermitage marked with a cross. The most likely interpre-tations are that it was either an allegory of Re-demption or the life of man, probably to be iden-tified as a painting requested by Isabella d'Este for her studiolo in Mantua.

Room 22 ❖ Flemish and German Renaissance

The decoration of this room, which originally housed the granducal collection of weapons, dates from 1588 (ceiling painted with grotesques and battle scenes by Ludovico Buti). It now holds a number of masterpieces by German and Flemish artists of the Renaissance. In addition to Holbein, Altdorfer and others, there is a series of paintings, mainly portraits, by Hans Memling, held in high esteem by artists such as Perugino and Italian clients, among them the Portinari, agents of the Medici family at Bruges.

The works

1. MASTER OF HOOGSTRÄTEN
*Madonna enthroned
with St. Catherine of Alexandria
and St. Barbara*
Early 16th century
Oil on canvas; 84x70
Inv. 1890 no. 1019

2. GÉRARD DAVID
Adoration of the Magi
c. 1490
Tempera on canvas; 95x80
Inv. 1890 no. 1029
Restored: 1999

**3. MASTER OF THE VIRGO
INTER VIRGINES**
Crucifixion
Late 15th century
Oil on wood
57x47
Inv. 1890 no. 1237

**4. PERUGINESQUE ARTIST
(FORMERLY ATTR. TO
JOOS VAN CLEVE)**
Mater Dolorosa
(copy from Memling)
Early 16th century
Oil on wood; 55x33.5
Inv. 1890 no. 1084

5. BERNART VAN ORLEY
*Portraits of an Unknown man and
of his wife*
c. 1521-1525
Oil on wood
32x29, 37x29
Inv. 1890 nos. 1140, 1161

6. JOOS VAN CLEVE
*Portraits of an Unknown man and
of his wife*
1527
Oil on wood
57x42 (each)
Inv. 1890 nos. 1643, 1644

7. HANS HOLBEIN THE YOUNGER
Portrait of Sir Richard Southwell
Dated 1536
Oil on wood
47.5x38
Inv. 1890 no. 1087

**8. HANS HOLBEIN
THE YOUNGER**
Self-portrait
1540-1543
Colored pastels on paper
32x26
Inv. 1890 no. 1630

9. ALBRECHT ALTDORFER
Martyrdom of St. Florian
c. 1516-1525
Oil on wood; 76.4x67.2
Dep. Inv. no. 4
Restored: 1980

10. ALBRECHT ALTDORFER
Leave-taking of St. Florian
c. 1516-1525
Oil on wood
81.4x67
Dep. Inv. no. 5

**11. SCHOOL OF HANS HOLBEIN
THE YOUNGER**
Portrait of a Man
(the so-called *Thomas More*)
c. 1530-1543
Oil on wood
42x36
Inv. 1890 no. 1120

12. HANS MEMLING
*Madonna and Child
enthroned with
two Musical angels*
c. 1480
Oil on wood
57x42
Inv. 1890 no. 1024

13. HANS MEMLING
*Portrait of a Man
with landscape*
c. 1470
Oil on wood
37x26
Inv. 1890 no. 1102

14. HANS MEMLING
Portrait of an Unknown man
c. 1490
Oil on wood
35x25
Inv. 1890 no. 1101

15. HANS MEMLING
*Portrait
of an Unknown man*
c. 1490
Oil on wood
35x24
Inv. 1890 no. 9970

16. HANS MEMLING
St. Benedict
c. 1487
Oil on wood
45.5x34.5
Inv. 1890 no. 1100

17. HANS MEMLING
*Portrait of Benedetto
di Tommaso Portinari*
Dated 1487
Oil on wood
45x34
Inv. 1890 no. 1090

**18. MASTER OF THE
BARONCELLI PORTRAITS**
*Portraits of Pierantonio
Baroncelli and his wife
Maria Bonciani*
c. 1489
Oil on wood
59x31 (each)
Inv. 1890 nos. 1036, 8405
Restored: 2002

19. GEORG PENCZ
Portrait of a Young man
Initialed and dated 1544
Oil on wood
91x70
Inv. 1890 no. 1891

20. LUCA DI LEIDA
*Christ with the Crown
of thorns*
First decades
of the 16th century
Oil on wood
130x85
Inv. 1890 no. 1460
Restored: 1985

.X°. IVLII. ANNO.
.H. VIII. XXVIII°.

ETATIS SVÆ
ANNO XXXIII.

❼

HANS HOLBEIN THE YOUNGER
Portrait of Sir Richard Southwell

Requested as a gift in 1620 by Cosimo de' Medici II from Thomas Howard, Duke of Arundel, this work dates back to the mature phase of the great portraitist from Augsburg, who was active for a long time at the English court.

Holbein investigates the man's face with scrupulous accuracy, and pauses over every fold of his clothing.
The original ebony frame of this painting is lost; beneath the painting four silver medallions remain displaying the coats of arms of the Medici, of the Arundels, of Southwell, and the name of the painter.

ALBRECHT ALTDORFER
Martyrdom of St. Florian

Painted by one of the most important representatives of the 16th century Danube school, this panel painting is part of an altarpiece portraying episodes from the life of the saint. Probably from the church of St. Florian near Linz

(Austria), it is now divided amongst various museums (one panel painting, the *Leave-taking of St. Florian*, is exhibited in this room).
Under a cloudy sky, this fragment showing a landscape is particularly effective, with its foreshortening from beneath a wooden bridge upon which the crowded scene of the martyrdom is taking place.

Room 23 ❖ Mantegna and Correggio

This is the end of the series of rooms parallel to the First Corridor and, like the previous two, formed part of the original armoury decorated with frescoes by Ludovico Buti (1588). On the ceiling are illustrations showing the manufacture of arms, of particular interest for the portrayal of the workshops of the period, with swords, lances and breastplates being forged. Other sections show cannons, the making of gunpowder, and the building of a fort. Today the room contains works by the Emilian painter Correggio and the Paduan Andrea Mantegna; by the latter we find the so-called Triptych, *a tiny panel painting of the* Madonna of the Rocks, *and the* Portrait of Cardinal Carlo de' Medici.

The works

1. CORREGGIO
*The Virgin adoring
the Christ Child*
c. 1524-1526
Oil on canvas; 82x68.3
Inv. 1890 no. 1453

2. CORREGGIO
Rest on the flight to Egypt
c. 1515-1517
Oil on canvas
125.5x106.5
Inv. 1890 no. 1455

3. CORREGGIO
*Madonna and Child
in glory*
c. 1510-1515
Oil on wood
20x16.3
Inv. 1890 no. 1329

**4. LEONARDESQUE PAINTER
(ATTR. TO FERRANDO SPAGNOLO)**
Leda
c. 1505-1507
Oil and resin on wood
130x77.5
Inv. 1890 no. 9953
Work acquired
by Rodolfo Siviero

5. GIOVANNI AMBROGIO DE' PREDIS
Portrait of a Man
Late 15th-early 16th century
Oil on wood
60x45
Inv. 1890 no. 1494

6. GIOVAN ANTONIO BOLTRAFFIO
(below)
Narcissus at the spring
Early 16th century
Tempera on wood
19x31
Inv. 1890 no. 2184

7. BOCCACCIO BOCCACCINO (above)
Gypsy girl
c. 1516-1518
Tempera on wood
24x19
Inv. 1890 no. 8539

8. IL SODOMA
Christ amidst his tormentors
Second-third decade
of the 16th century
Tempera on wood, 85x60
Inv. 1890 no. 738

9. ALESSANDRO ARALDI
*Portrait [presumed]
of Barbara Pallavicino*
Second decade of the 16th century
Tempera on wood
46.5x35
Inv. 1890 no. 8383

10. VINCENZO FOPPA
Madonna and Child with Angel
c. 1479-1480
Tempera on wood
41x32.5
Inv. 1890 no. 9492

11. ANDREA MANTEGNA
Madonna of the Rocks
Variously dated around 1466
or between 1488 and 1490
Tempera on wood
29x21.5
Inv. 1890 no. 1348

12. ANDREA MANTEGNA
*Adoration of the Magi,
Ascension and Circumcision*
Variously painted
from about 1462 to 1470
Tempera on wood
77x75 (central panel)
86x42.5 (side panels)
Inv. 1890 no. 910

13. ANDREA MANTEGNA
*Portrait of Cardinal
Carlo de' Medici*
c. 1466
Tempera on wood
41.3x29.5
Inv. 1890 no. 994

14. GIAMPIETRINO
*St. Catherine
of Alexandria*
Third decade
of the 16th century
Tempera on wood
64x50
Inv. 1890 no. 8544

15. BERNARDINO LUINI
*The executioner
presents John
the Baptist's head
to Herodias*
c. 1527-1531
Tempera on wood
51x58
Inv. 1890 no. 1454

16. BERNARDINO DE' CONTI
Portrait of a Man
c. 1500
Tempera on wood
42x32
Inv. 1890 no. 1883

**17. GIOVANNI FRANCESCO
DE' MAINERI**
Christ carrying the Cross
Early 16th century
Tempera on wood
42x50
Inv. 1890 no. 3348

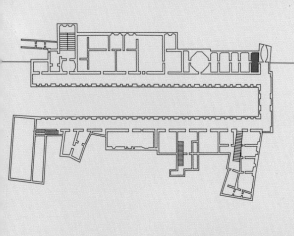

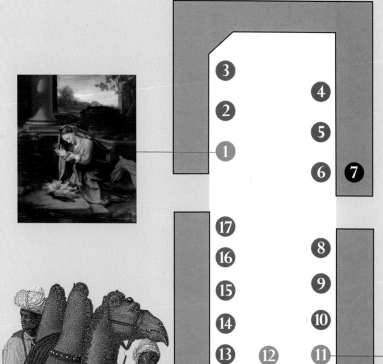

❶

CORREGGIO
The Virgin adoring the Christ Child

A gift in 1617 from the Duke of Mantua to Cosimo de' Medici II, this work was immediately placed in the Tribune, where it remained until the end of the 19th century. With poetic fore-shortening, lit perhaps by the light of a sunset, the young Madonna kneels and gazes adoringly at her Child, in a scene of tranquil and effective balance. The work dates to the middle phase of the Emilian artist's activity, shortly preceding the "greatly foreshortened" fresco decoration of the cupola in Parma Cathedral.

11

ANDREA MANTEGNA
Madonna of the Rocks

At the time when Vasari mentioned this "little painting" in 1568, it already belonged to Francesco de' Medici, who was later to become Grand Duke. Some experts believe that this is the painting promised Lorenzo de' Medici in 1484 by the great master from Padua, as can be read in a letter he addressed to the Magnificent. It seems more probable however that Vasari was right when he stated that the painting was executed by Mantegna in Rome between 1488 and 1490. Apparently basic and essential, the work is rich in symbolic allusions. Against the background of a harsh, rocky landscape, stonecutters working on a column can be glimpsed on the right, and a tomb is visible below – an allusion to Christ's Sepulchre and thus a prediction of the destiny of the Child lying in the Virgin's lap.

ANDREA MANTEGNA
The Adoration of the Magi
The Ascension (opposite page, left)
and *The Circumcision* (opposite page, right)

This panel showing the *Adoration of the Magi*, painted separately on a slightly concave surface, was inserted in 1827 into a non-original frame to form an arbitrary triptych together with the two panels illustrated on the opposite page, the *Ascension* and the *Circumcision*. Owned by the Medici from at least 1587, the three paintings had first been the property of the Gonza-

ga family of Mantua. They are generally believed to be identified with the "small but very beautiful scenes with figures", mentioned by Giorgio Vasari in 1550 as decorations for the chapel of the Castle of San Giorgio in Mantua. We know in fact, from letters by Ludovico Gonzaga, that Mantegna had been invited to court since 1459, a period near the time when at least one of the three panels was begun. The paintings differ however in both style and size, and are very probably from different periods. In any case, this may have been the painter's first commission from the Mantuan court, where

he was later to paint a fresco in the famous *Room of the Bride and Groom*. By the middle of the 15ᵗʰ century, the Mantuan artistic scene was already adopting a taste for the classical, owing to the presence of sculptors like Pisanello, Donatello and architects such as Leon Battista Alberti and Luca Fancelli from Fiesole. It is not surprising that Mantegna was invited to take part since he was undoubtedly, amongst northern Italian painters, one of the most receptive to the classical revival. This is especially evident in the right-hand panel, whose scene is set in a sumptuous polychrome marble interi-or with classical-style reliefs, so different from the *Ascension* painting, dominated by a rugged and rocky landscape. In the *Adoration of the Magi*, the range of brilliant colours, typical of the Lombard-Venetian culture, is combined with a powerfully scenic composition.

The concave form of the panel's wooden support suggests that the painting was perhaps destined for the rear wall of the chapel of the Castle of San Giorgio, creating a niche over the altar. The vertical panels may instead have been inserted into gold frames on the other walls of the room.

Room 24 ❖ Cabinet of Miniatures

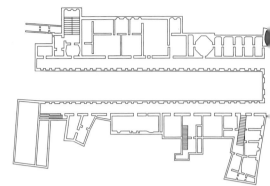

This small room contains more than 400 miniatures from the grand-ducal collections. Originally known as "The Chamber of Idols" for the antique bronzes, Mexican objects, and works in gold displayed here, the room was then given the name, "Madam's Chamber", and from 1589 contained the jewels of Christine of Lorraine, wife of Ferdinando I. It then housed the Medicean collection of classical gems and cameos until 1928 (now at the Medici Treasures in Pitti Palace established by the Grand Duke Pietro Leopoldo (1781). Zanobi del Rosso was the architect responsible and Filippo Lucci painted the fresco, Allegory of Fame, *on the vault. The miniatures on display are small portraits from various eras and schools, subsequently mounted into small composits. They come from a great number of collections constituted between 1664 and 1675 by Cardinal Leopoldo de' Medici. The Cardinal was at the same time increasing his collections of self-portraits and drawings. The miniatures were in part purchased by Paolo del Sera, his agent in Venice, and by other intermediaries. Some of the pieces are heirlooms while others were commissioned by Leopoldo of artists active in Florence. Hung above the pictures are six noteworthy parchments, including reproductions of famous paintings by Raphael and Titian which were once in the Medicean collection.*

Second and Third Corridor and Loggia (First Floor)

The rearrangement of the Second and Third Corridors was carried out at the same time as the restoration of the First Corridor in 1996. With its large glass windows facing the Uffizi Square and the Arno River, the South Corridor is famous for its views. Among the sculptures exhibited are a Roman copy of the Praxitelic torso of Apollo Sauroktonos, *restored and completed in the 16th century, and the Roman copy of* Cupid and Psyche. *At the intersection with the East Corridor, the ceilings are painted with frescoes in the grotesque style, dating back to Francesco I (1581). Those facing west show the glorification of the Medici family (Nasini and Tonelli) and date back to Cosimo III (1670-1723). Above the windows facing the river are the later portraits of the Giovio Series, which continue into the Third Corridor together with canvas paintings from the 17th to the beginning of the 19th century, spaced alternately with paintings from the Aulic Series, many of which have been restored. On the side of the doors of the Third Corridor hang 50 portraits of the Lorraine dynasty. Following the evidence of an 18th century drawing in the* Album of De Greyss, *the famous Roman* Wild Boar *has been reinstalled at the end of the corridor towards the Loggia dei Lanzi. This, along with the small replica of a* Farnese Hercules, *is placed beside the* Laocoon *by Baccio Bandinelli (c. 1520-1525), the first copy from the original of the Hellenistic group found in Rome in 1506. All three sculptures were restored in 1994. Since March 2004 the Loggia on the first floor has been open to the public.*

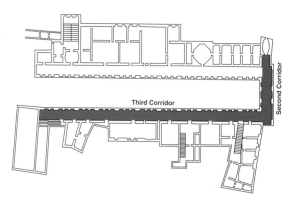

The statues

Second Corridor

1. *Sleeping Cupid*
Roman copy
of a Hellenistic
original
Black marble
Inv. 1914 no. 279

2. *Lance-thrower*
Roman copy,
1st century AD,
of a bronze original
by Polyclitus
(450-440 BC)
Pentelic marble
Inv. 1914 no. 91

3. ATTICIANO DI AFRODISIA
Terpsichore
4th century AD
Pentelic marble
signed on the base
Inv. 1914 no. 269

4. *Demeter*
Roman copy of a
Hellenistic original
from the late 4th century BC
Greek marble
Inv. 1914 no. 120

5. *Seated Nymph*
Roman copy of a
bronze original from
the second half of
the 2nd century BC
Pentelic marble
Inv. 1914 no. 190

6. *Leda*
Roman copy,
2nd century AD,
of an original by Timotheos
(380-370 BC),
restored by G. B. Foggini
Pentelic marble
Inv. 1914 no. 263

7. *Wolf*
Roman copy from the time
of Hadrian of an original
from the 5th century BC
Porphyry
Without inv. no.

8. 17TH CENTURY SCULPTOR
completing of a torso
from the Hellenistic period
Cupid
White marble
Inv. 1914 no. 170
Restored: 1995

9. *Cupid and Psyche*
Roman copy
of a Hellenistic original
from the late 4th century BC
Luni marble
Inv. 1914 no. 339

10. *Venus*
Roman copy of an original
from the 5th century BC
Greek marble
Inv. 1914 no. 27

11. *Copy of torso
of Apollo Sauroktonos*
Roman copy of a bronze torso
by Praxiteles (365-350 BC),
completed as *Apollo Musician*
by G. B. Caccini (c. 1585)
Opaque white marble
for the ancient torso
and coloured marble
Inv. 1914 no. 249
Restored: 1995

12. *Pothos*
Roman copy, in counter-part,
of an original by Skopas
(340-330 BC)
Pentelic marble
Inv. 1914 no. 165

Third Corridor

13. ROMAN COPIER FROM THE 2ND CENTURYAD, MINO DA FIESOLE AND GIOVAN BATTISTA FOGGINI
"Red" Marsyas
Marble "pavonazzetto"
(ancient part) and white
(modern additions)
Inv. 1914 no. 201. Restored: 1992

14. ROMAN COPIER FROM THE 2ND CENTURY AD AND MODERN SCULPTORS, INCLUDING FRANCESCO CARRADORI
"White" Marsyas
White marble (insular?)
Inv. 1914 no. 199

15. *Aesculapius*
Second half of 2nd century AD
Marble
Inv. 1914 no. 252

16. 17TH CENTURY SCULPTOR
completing a torso
from Roman times
Venus
Various types of marble
and Parian marble
Inv. 1914 no. 251
Restored: 1995

17. *Mercury*
Roman copy, from the time
of Antonius, of an original
from the 4th century BC
Pentelic marble
Inv. 1914 no. 147

18. *Attis*
From the time of Hadrian,
restored by Francesco Franchi
(signature and date, 1712,
on the base)
Greek marble
Inv. 1914 no. 84

19. *Daphnis*
Roman copy of an original
from the 1st century BC
with late Renaissance additions
Parian marble
Inv. 1914 no. 253

20. *Vestal*
Roman copy of an original
from the Hellenistic age
Greek marble
Inv. 1914 no. 281

21. *Victory*
Roman copy from the time
of Hadrian of an original
of praxitelean influence
Pentelic marble
Inv. 1914 no. 101

22. *Pothos*
Roman copy, in counter-part,
of an original by Skopas
(340-330 BC)
Pentelic marble
Inv. 1914 no. 261

23. *Wounded Warrior*
Greek-Ionic original
from the last third
of the 5th century BC,
with modern additions
Medium-grain Parian marble
and other marbles
Inv. 1914 no. 252
Restored: 1992

24. *Ganymede*
Roman copy
of an original from
the Hellenistic age
Veined white marble
Inv. 1914 no. 128

25. *Seated Apollo*
Roman copy
from Imperial
times of a
Hellenistic original
Greek marble
Inv. 1914 no. 240
Restored: 1995

26. *Hygea*
Roman copy from
Imperial times of
an original
from the mid-4th century BC
Greek marble
Inv. 1914 no. 214

27. *Muse*
Roman copy,
middle of 1st century AD,
of a Hellenistic
original
Italic and Greek marble
Inv. 1914 no. 117

28. *Jove*
Roman copy,
2nd century AD,
of an original influenced
by Phydias
Greek marble
Inv. 1914 no. 223

29. 16TH CENTURY SCULPTOR
completing a torso
from Roman times
Bacchus
Greek marble
Inv. 1914 no. 258

30. *Statue of woman wearing a peplum (Juno)*
Roman copy
of an original
from the 5th century BC
Greek marble
Inv. 1914 no. 231
Restored: 1995

31. *Apollo*
Roman copy
of an original
from the Hellenistic age,
restored
by Flaminio Vacca
in the 16th century
Greek marble
Inv. 1914 no. 162

32. *Standing woman with portrait head*
2nd century AD
Veined Greek marble
Inv. 1914 no. 149

33. *Pan and Daphnis*
Roman copy,
late 2nd-early 3rd
century AD,
of a late
Hellenistic original
Pentelic marble
Inv. 1914 no. 92

34. *Minerva of the Rospigliosi type*
Roman copy
from Imperial times
of an Attic original,
second half
of the 4th century BC
Greek marble
Inv. 1914 no. 185
Restored: 1995

35. *Standing woman, known as the "Great Herculanian"*
Replica from the 2nd century AD
Greek marble
Inv. 1914 no. 197

36. *Standing woman*
Roman copy,
2nd century AD,
of a Hellenistic
original
Greek marble
Inv. 1914 no. 30

37. *Nereid on a seahorse*
Roman copy,
1st century AD,
of a Hellenistic
original
Parian marble
Inv. 1914 no. 208
Restored: 1995

38. *Hercules of the Farnese type*
Roman copy,
2nd century AD,
of an original by Lysippus
(c. 320 BC)
Greek and statuary marble
Inv. 1914 no. 138
Restored: 1994

39. BACCIO BANDINELLI
Laocoon
Copy of the
Hellenistic group
in the Vatican Museums
c. 1520-1525
Marble
Inv. 1914 no. 284
Restored: 1994

40. *Wild boar*
Roman copy,
1st century AD,
of a Hellenistic
bronze original
from the 3rd century BC
Pentelic marble
Inv. 1914 no. 63
Restored: 1994

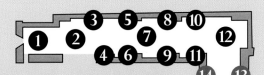

View of the Second Corridor or South Corridor

FLORENTINE SCHOOL
Grotesque Decoration (Second Corridor)

The 'trompe l'œil' pergolas, frescoed around 1581, are bordered with coats of arms of the Medici family, the House of Austria (the first wife of Francesco I was Jean of Austria), and Bianca Cappello, lover and then second wife of the Grand Duke. The emblem of Cappello, who was disliked by the Medicis, was previously covered but later found during restoration.

Loggia (First Floor)

A. BARTOLOMEO AMMANNATI
Mars
Documented in 1559
Bronze
Height 215
Inv. 1914 no. 38
Restored: 1994

B. *Medicean Vase*
(from Villa Medici)
Neo-Attic art,

1st century BC
White Grecian marble
Height 173; diam. 135
Inv. 1914 no. 307

C. JACOPO DEL DUCA
*Silenus
and the Young Bacchus*
1571-1574
Bronze
Height 187
Inv. 1914 no. 33

Wild Boar
(Third Corridor)

The *Wild Boar* comes from the house of Paolo Ponti in Rome. Highly esteemed for its naturalism, the sculpture was damaged by a fire in 1762 and then restored. In 1634, Pietro Tacca made a copy of it for his bronze universally known as the "Porcellino" (Little Pig), which is now a highly popular attraction in the Mercato Nuovo.

123

Room 25 ❖ Michelangelo and the Florentine Painting

Room 25, dominated by a masterpiece by Michelangelo, is the first of eleven rooms now dedicated to 16th century painting. In what are now Rooms 25-33, the Grand Duke Ferdinando I in 1588 established workshops for the Minor Guilds and a Foundry for the distillation of perfumes, poisons and antidotes. In the mid-18th century, medals and gems were exhibited in Rooms 25-26, and at the end of the century, Venetian paintings of the 15th and the 16th century. Dedicated to 16th century works after the Second World War, this series of rooms has recently acquired a new, rigorously geographical layout which has been helped by the restoration following the 1993 bombing.

The works

1. FRA BARTOLOMEO
Portia
c. 1495
Tempera on wood
108x52
Inv. 1890 no. 8310
Restored: 1994

2. FRA BARTOLOMEO
Vision of St. Bernard
1507
Tempera on wood
215x231
Inv. 1890 no. 8455
Restored: 1992

3. FRA BARTOLOMEO
Del Pugliese Tabernacle:
Annunciation (front)
Presentation at the Temple
and *Nativity* (rear)
c. 1497
Oil on wood
19.5x9, 18x9
Inv. 1890 no. 1477

4. RIDOLFO DEL GHIRLANDAIO
(ATTR.)
Veiled woman (The Nun)
c. 1510
Oil on wood
65x48
Inv. 1890 no. 8380

5. ALONSO BERRUGUETE
Madonna with Child
c. 1517
Tempera on wood
89x64
Inv. 1890 no. 5852

6. ALONSO BERRUGUETE
Salome
1512-1516
Oil on canvas
87.5x71
Inv. 1890 no. 5374

7. MICHELANGELO BUONARROTI
Doni Tondo
(Holy Family with the infant
St. John the Baptist)

c. 1506-1508
Tempera on wood
Diam. 120,
with the frame 170
Inv. 1890 no. 1456
Restored: 1985

8. RIDOLFO DEL GHIRLANDAIO
(ATTR.)
Cover for a portrait
c. 1510
Oil on wood
73x50.3
Inv. 1890 no. 6042

9. FRANCESCO GRANACCI
Joseph led away to prison
c. 1515
Tempera on wood
95.7x130.5
Inv. 1890 no. 2150
Restored: 1995

10. FRANCESCO GRANACCI
AND WORKSHOP
Joseph presents
his father and brothers
to the Pharaoh
c. 1515
Tempera on wood
95x224
Inv. 1890 no. 2152
Restored: 1995

11. MARIOTTO ALBERTINELLI
Visitation
On the predella (from left):
Annunciation, Birth of Jesus
and *Presentation in the Temple*
Dated 1503 on the pillars
Oil on wood
232.5x146.5, 23x149.5 (predella)
Inv. 1890 nos. 1587, 1586
Restored: 1995

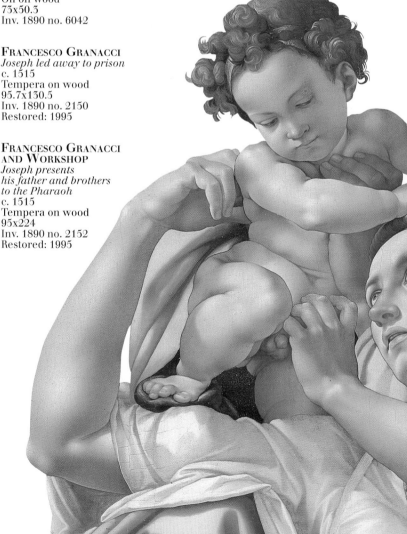

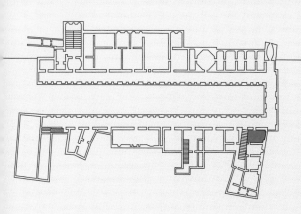

7

MICHELANGELO BUONARROTI
Doni Tondo
(Holy Family with the infant St. John the Baptist)

Rightly considered to be the most important and enigmatic painting of the 16th century, the *Doni Tondo* is the only example of Michelangelo's painting preserved in Florence, and the only painting on a movable support which can definitely be attributed to him. Executed for the Florentine merchant Agnolo Doni and his wife Maddalena Strozzi, possibly on the occasion of the birth of their daughter Maria (September 8, 1507), it was certainly painted after January 1506 when the *Laocoon* was found in Rome, a sculpture from which Michelangelo took the pose of the nude sitting behind St. Joseph. It is no coincidence that the postures of

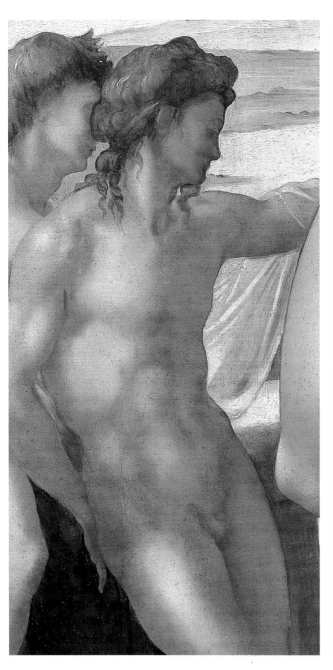 

the nudes are derived from many other classical sculptures known at the time. Michelangelo was in fact among the artists of his generation most strongly influenced by classical statuary, which he studied with great care. This unusual *Holy Family* in striking tones, a prelude to Mannerist art, shows three almost sculptural figures in the foreground in a strange and serpentine composition. The figure of the Virgin is taking Jesus from (or offering him to) St. Joseph. She is counterbalanced by five young nudes behind a small wall, who lean or sit on a balustrade, beyond which a simple landscape fades into the horizon. The meaning of this work is still uncertain; it may be inspired by the Biblical passages which refer to the birth and baptism of Christ, hinted at by the bust of the infant St. John to the right, and the five round lunettes on the frame showing Christ, angels and prophets.

Room 26 ❖ Raphael and Andrea del Sarto

This room is dominated by two key figures of the early 16th century: Raphael from Urbino and Andrea del Sarto from Florence. Raphael arrived in Florence near the end of 1504, at the time when Leonardo and Michelangelo were preparing the cartoons for the lost frescoes of the battle of Anghiari and the battle of Cascina in the Council Hall of the Republic in Palazzo Vecchio. At this crucial moment for Florentine art, Raphael was studying the cartoons by the two masters, frequenting painters such as Ridolfo del Ghirlandaio and painting for wealthy clients panels such as the Madonna of the Goldfinch *(now in restoration). In addition to the probable self-portrait and to paintings of uncertain attribution, this room contains important works by Raphael painted after his stay in Florence (among them the* Portrait of Pope Leo X*). Andrea del Sarto – an outstanding figure in the development of Mannerism in Florence – is represented here by the* Madonna of the Harpies, *as well as the Altarpiece of the Church of the Romitorio in the Vallombrosa monastery (the frame, a devotional image of the Madonna originally at the centre of the composition, and the predella with an* Annunciation *have been lost). The processional banner of the Confraternity of San Jacopo del Nicchio, previously in the Spedale degli Innocenti, is an intimately meditative work. Lastly, two intense portraits by Franciabigio and by Puligo reveal the influence of Andrea on his contemporaries.*

The works

1. ANDREA DEL SARTO
Banner of St. James of Nicchio
(St. James with the children)
c. 1528
Oil on canvas
155.5x85.6
Inv. 1890 no. 1583
Restored: 1988

2. ANDREA DEL SARTO
Madonna of the Harpies
Signed and dated 1517
Tempera on wood
207x178
Inv. 1890 no. 1577
Restored: 1984

3. RAPHAEL (ATTR.)
Portrait of Guidubaldo
da Montefeltro
Variously dated from 1506 to 1508
Oil on wood
70.5x49.9
Inv. 1890 no. 8538

4. RAPHAEL (ATTR.)
Portrait of Elisabetta Gonzaga
Variously dated from 1502 to 1506
Oil on wood
52.5x37.3
Inv. 1890 no. 1441

5. RAPHAEL
Portrait of a Young man (the so-called
Francesco Maria della Rovere)
c. 1503-1504
Tempera on wood
48x35.5
Inv. 1890 no. 8760
Restored: 1989

6. RAPHAEL (ATTR.)
Self-portrait
c. 1506
Tempera on wood
47.5x33
Inv. 1890 no. 1706

7. RAPHAEL
Madonna of the Goldfinch
c. 1505-1506
Tempera on wood
107x77.2
Inv. 1890 no. 1447
In restoration

8. RAPHAEL
Portrait of Pope Leo X
with Cardinals Giulio de' Medici
and Luigi de' Rossi
1518
Oil on wood
155.5x119.5
Inv. 1912 no. 40
Restored: 1996

9. RAPHAEL AND WORKSHOP
Portrait of Pope Julius II
c. 1512
Tempera on wood
108.5x80
Inv. 1890 no. 1450

10. RAPHAEL (ATTR.)
Portrait of a Man
(formerly thought to be
a Portrait of Perugino)
c. 1505-1506
Tempera on wood, 51x37
Inv. 1890 no. 1482
Restored: 1996

11. FRANCIABIGIO
Portrait of a Young man
Initialed and dated 1514
Tempera on wood
59.4x46.3
Inv. 1890 no. 8381
Restored: 1989

12. ANDREA DEL SARTO
Vallombrosa Altarpiece
(Altar frontal
of the four Saints)
Dated 1528
Tempera on wood
184x86 (panel with saints)
76x42 (angels)
23.5x89.5 (left predella)
23.5x91.5 (right predella)
Inv. 1890 nos. 8394-8396
Restored: 1986

13. ANDREA DEL SARTO
Portrait of a Woman
with a basket
of spindles
c. 1515
Oil on wood
76x54
Inv. 1890 no. 1480
Restored: 1996

14. DOMENICO PULIGO
Portrait
of Pietro Carnesecchi
c. 1527
Tempera on wood
59.5x39.5
Inv. 1890 no. 1489

ANDREA DEL SARTO
Madonna of the Harpies

Begun in 1515 for the Sisters of San Francesco de' Macci, the painting was not completed as required. With the St. John the Evangelist, requested in the contract, a St. Francis was added beside the Virgin and Child instead of St. Bonaventure. The work takes its name, following a mistake of Vasari, from the monsters ("Harpies") in bas-relief on the base. Antonio Natali has instead demonstrated that they are locusts, according to the complex theological significance of the painting, alluding to the ninth chapter of St. John's *Apocalypse*.

RAPHAEL (ATTR.)
Self-portrait

The subject and paternity of this famous portrait, which arrived in the Gallery in 1682 as part of Cardinal Leopold's collection of self-portraits and was restored in 1983, have long been hotly debated. Now that examinations have revealed a drawing of excellent quality under the painted surface, the most traditional hypothesis – that this is a self-portrait of Raphael as a young man, painted by the artist from Urbino in about 1506, at the time of his stay in Florence – seems highly probable. Raphael went to Florence in 1504 "to learn", thanks to a letter of presentation from Giovanna Feltria, the Duchess of Soria.

7

RAPHAEL
Madonna of the Goldfinch

Painted for the merchant Lorenzo Nasi at the time of his marriage to Sandra Canigiani (1505), this famous panel was damaged in 1547 when the house on Via de' Bardi collapsed. The young Raphael, who had been in Florence for about a year, here experimented for the first time with a group of figures centred in the foreground, against a backdrop of a Leonardesque landscape. The Virgin is seated with a book in one hand and her Son between her knees. He caresses the goldfinch offered to him by the infant St. John.

8

RAPHAEL
*Portrait of Pope Leo X with Cardinals
Giulio de' Medici and Luigi de' Rossi*

The portrait of Leo X (Giovanni de' Medici, 1475-1521, elected Pope in 1513) arrived in Florence from Rome in 1518. It was later praised by Vasari for its figures which are "not fake, but painted in full relief", for the "rustling and shining" damask robe, for the "soft and realistic" fur linings, for the golden knob on the chair which reflects "the light from the windows, the Pope's shoulders, and the surrounding room". The restoration has suggested that the two cardinals may be by another hand.

Room 27 ❖ Pontormo and Rosso Fiorentino

This room is consecrated to the two greatest figures in Florentine Mannerism (represented in the Tribune). Almost from the beginning, Pontormo and Rosso split with their master Andrea del Sarto, to inaugurate a language of "disruption". Works by the court portrait painter Agnolo Bronzino and artists of primary importance for the development of 16th century painting, such as the Sienese Beccafumi with his intense Self-portrait, are also displayed here.

The works

1. AGNOLO BRONZINO (below)
Pygmalion and Galatea
Variously dated
from 1529 to 1532
Oil on wood
81x64 (with vertical extensions)
Inv. 1890 no. 9936

2. BACHIACCA (above)
Christ before Caiaphas
c. 1535-1540
Tempera on wood
50.5x41
Inv. 1890 no. 8407

3. BACHIACCA (below)
Stories of St. Acacio
c. 1521
Tempera on wood
37.5x256
Inv. 1890 no. 877

4. BACHIACCA (above on the left)
Deposition from the Cross
c. 1517-1518
Tempera on wood
93x71
Inv. 1890 no. 511

5. MIRABELLO CAVALORI
(ATTR., TRADITIONALLY
ATTRIBUTED TO PONTORMO,
IN COLLABORATION WITH
BRONZINO) (above on the right)
Madonna and Child,
two Angels,
and Sts. Francis
and Jerome
c. 1524 (if Pontormo)
c. 1565 (if Cavalori)
Oil on wood
73x61
Inv. 1890 no. 1538

6. ROSSO FIORENTINO (below)
Portrait of a Girl
c. 1514-1515
Tempera on wood
45x33
Inv. 1890 no. 3245

7. PIER FRANCESCO
DI IACOPO FOSCHI (above)
Portrait of a Man
c. 1530-1540
Tempera on wood
65x50
Inv. 1890 no. 1483

8. PIER FRANCESCO DI IACOPO FOSCHI
(FORMERLY ATTR. TO
PONTORMO) (below)
Portrait of a Musician
1520-1530
Oil on wood, 88x67
Inv. 1890 no. 743
Restored: 1994

9. GIORGIO DI GIOVANNI
(FORMERLY ATTR.
TO DOMENICO BECCAFUMI) (above)
Flight of Clelia
and the Roman virgins
c. 1525-1530
Oil on wood, 74x122
Inv. 1890 no. 6057

10. PONTORMO (ATTR.) (below)
Portrait of Maria Salviati
Variously dated c. 1530-1534
and c. 1543-1545
Tempera on wood, 87x71
Inv. 1890 no. 3565
Restored: 1995

11. DOMENICO BECCAFUMI (above)
Holy Family
with the infant St. John
c. 1518-1520
Tempera on wood
diam. 84
Inv. 1890 no. 780

12. PONTORMO
Nativity of St. John
c. 1526
Tempera on wood
(on the back are the Della Casa
and Tornaquinci coats of arms)
diam. 59
Inv. 1890 no. 1532

13. ROSSO FIORENTINO
(OR CONTEMPORARY COPY?)
Moses defends the
daughters of Jethro
c. 1523
Oil on linen, 160x117
Inv. 1890 no. 2151
Restored: 1995

14. ROSSO FIORENTINO (ATTR.)
Portrait of a Young man in black
c. 1515
Tempera on wood
83x64
San Marco and Cenacoli Inv. no. 106

15. ROSSO FIORENTINO
Madonna of the Spedalingo
(Madonna with
Child and Saints)
1518
Tempera on wood
172x141
Inv. 1890 no. 3190
Restored: 1995

16. PONTORMO
St. Anthony Abbot
c. 1518-1519
Oil on canvas
78x66
Inv. 1890 no. 8379

17. DOMENICO BECCAFUMI
Self-portrait
c. 1527
Oil on paper on wood
31.3x22.6
Inv. 1890 no. 1731
Restored: 1990

18. AGNOLO BRONZINO
Lamentation
over the Dead Christ
c. 1546-1548
Tempera on wood
115x100
Inv. 1890 no. 8545

19. PONTORMO
The Supper at Emmaus
1525
Oil on canvas
230x173
Inv. 1890 no. 8740
Restored: 1994

20. AGNOLO BRONZINO
The Panciatichi Holy Family
(Holy Family
with the infant St. John)
c. 1540
Tempera on wood
117x93
Inv. 1890 no. 8377

21. AGNOLO BRONZINO
(ALSO ATTR. TO PONTORMO)
Martyrdom of the eleven
thousand Martyrs
c. 1530-1532
Tempera on wood
64x45
Inv. 1890 no. 1525

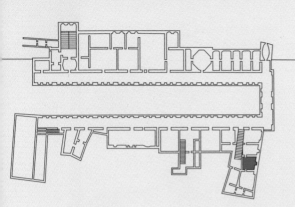

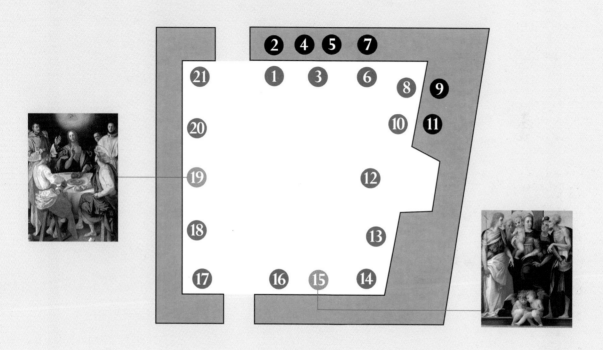

⑮

ROSSO FIORENTINO
Madonna dello Spedalingo
(Madonna with Child and Saints)

In 1518 Leonardo Buonafé, rector of the Santa Maria Nuova Hospital (the "Spedalingo"), commissioned an altarpiece for the church of Ognissanti. According to Vasari, the sketch of the painting was refused by Buonafé, because the saints looked like "devils", customary for Rosso, who, in the end, "sweetened" the "bitter and desperate expressions" painted in the oil sketches. The altarpiece with its very unusual figures did not reach Ognissanti, and the painting of Buonafé's namesake St. Leonard was then substituted by a St. Stephen with the stone of his martyrdom on his head.

19

PONTORMO
The Supper at Emmaus

This panel was painted in 1525 for the guest-room of the Charterhouse in Galluzzo south of Florence, where Pontormo had spent a peaceful period of time in 1523. The Apparition of Christ to the Apostles is portrayed on this altarpiece with intense spirituality. Inspired by a Dürer etching, an artist whose work Pontormo often studied at this time, the painting nevertheless reveals an independent style, theatrical in its surprising touches of light and detailed observation of everyday life (the friar to the left is the elder Leonardo Buonafé, then prior of the Charterhouse). The holy eye, symbol of the Trinity, was added later.

Room 28 ❖ Titian and Sebastiano del Piombo

In the 18th century this room was used as a service area and held no works of art. Only in the early 20th century was a group of 16th century paintings, mainly Venetian, placed here, while today the room is dedicated to Giorgione's two highest "creations", according to Giorgio Vasari's 16th century definition: the great Titian and Sebastiano del Piombo, the latter active first in Venice and then in Rome. Some of the Uffizi's most famous masterpieces are gathered here, as testimony to the collections of Venetian paintings highly esteemed by the Medici family, and painted in a style very different from that of the Tuscans; to put it briefly, in Tuscany the emphasis was on drawing, in the Veneto, on colour. Ranked among the greatest portrait painters of all times, and certainly among the most famous, Titian is represented here by the seductive beauty of the Venus of Urbino *and the equally alluring* Flora – *in the Uffizi since 1793 – as well as by intense portraits praised already by his contemporaries for their "liveliness", their portrayal of interior as well as superficial aspects. Sebastiano del Piombo, to whom* The Sick Man, *now recognised as a work by Titian, was once attributed, is represented by a famous portrait of a woman known as* The "Fornarina", *which was in the Tribune already in 1589. Some works by Palma the Elder, one of the most significant interpreters of Giorgione's art, are also displayed here.*

The works

1. **JACOPO PALMA THE ELDER AND WORKSHOP**
Holy Family with the infant St. John and the Magdalene
First quarter of the 16th century
Oil on wood, 87x117
Inv. 1890 no. 950
Restored: 1989

2. **JACOPO PALMA THE ELDER**
Judith
c. 1525-1528
Oil on wood
90x71
Inv. 1890 no. 939

3. **JACOPO PALMA THE ELDER**
Resurrection of Lazarus
c. 1510
Oil on wood
94x110
Inv. 1890 no. 3256

4. **TITIAN**
Portrait of Bishop Ludovico Beccadelli
Signed and dated 1552
Oil on canvas
117.5x97
Inv. 1890 no. 1457

5. **TITIAN**
Portrait of a Knight of Malta
c. 1515
Oil on canvas
80x64
Inv. 1890 no. 942
Restored: 1998

6. **TITIAN**
Madonna of the Roses
c. 1520-1530
Oil on wood
69x96.5
Inv. 1890 no. 952
Restored: 2002

7. **TITIAN**
Flora
c. 1515-1517
Oil on canvas
79.7x63.5
Inv. 1890 no. 1462
Restored: 1993

8. **TITIAN**
Portrait of a Man (The Sick Man)
Dated 1514
(perhaps not the painter's own handwriting)
Oil on canvas, 81x60
Inv. 1890 no. 2183

9. **TITIAN AND WORKSHOP**
Portrait of Pope Sixtus IV
c. 1540-1545
Oil on wood; 109.5x87
Inv. 1890 no. 744
Restored: 2002

10. **SEBASTIANO DEL PIOMBO**
The death of Adonis
c. 1512
Oil on canvas
189x285
Inv. 1890 no. 916
Restored: 1994

11. **SEBASTIANO DEL PIOMBO**
Portrait of a Woman (The "Fornarina")
Dated 1512
Oil on wood
68x55
Inv. 1890 no. 1443

12. **TITIAN**
Portrait of Francesco Maria della Rovere
1536-1538
Oil on canvas
114x103
Inv. 1890 no. 926

13. **TITIAN**
The Venus of Urbino
1538
Oil on canvas
119x165
Inv. 1890 no. 1437
Restored: 1996

14. **TITIAN**
Portrait of Eleonora Gonzaga della Rovere
1536-1538
Oil on canvas
114x103
Inv. 1890 no. 919

15. **TITIAN AND WORKSHOP**
St. Margaret and the dragon
c. 1565-1570
Oil on canvas
116.5x98
Inv. 1890 no. 928

TITIAN
Flora

This much-admired, sensual painting was in Alfonso Lopez's collection in Amsterdam; it arrived at the Uffizi in 1641 in an exchange with the Imperial Gallery of Vienna.

This is almost certainly a portrait of a young bride, who rather timidly reveals her breast with one hand, whilst with the other, on which she wears a barely visible wedding band, she holds a bouquet of flowers. This beauty with her long, loosened hair and intense expression represents Flora, Goddess of Fertility.

10

SEBASTIANO DEL PIOMBO
The death of Adonis

Painted in Rome for the patron Agostino Chigi, who since 1511 had been asking the Venetian artist to fresco his villa, the Farnesina, this canvas was in the Pitti Palace in 1587, and in 1675 in the collection of Cardinal Leopoldo. Ripped in 1993 and restored immediately, it is a symbol of the Uffizi's renewal after the bomb. Possibly identifiable as the painting with "mostly nude and beautiful figures" in a 1520 inventory of the Villa Farnesina, it is filled with cultural allusions and references whose meanings are still debated. The subject is inspired by the desperation of Venus at the death of Adonis (left). Venus sits naked in the foreground in a posture presumably taken from the classical Boy Removing a Thorn from his Foot. The painting may hide a moralistic meaning around the lament of *Venice-Venusia* (*Venus = Venusia*), the city which appears in the background with its famous monuments: the Ducal Palace, the domes of the Palatine Basilica, the Clock Tower, and the Vecchie Procuratie. In this mythological evocation, Venice appears to be absorbed by the seductions of sensual beauty and is destined to death and putrefaction (Adonis killed by the boar).

⓭

TITIAN
The Venus of Urbino

Commissioned in 1538 by Guidubaldo della Rovere, the Duke of Urbino, this is one of the most famous erotic images of all time, a cultural icon. A young girl with blond hair flowing loosely over her shoulders, looks knowingly but allusively at the spectator. She is completely naked, lying on a luxurious bed with rumpled sheets; her left hand resting over the pubic area as if to hide it is in fact ambiguously inviting. In her right hand she holds a small posy of roses, a symbol of love reiterated by the myrtle plant on the window-sill.

The little dog sleeping on the bed, symbolises fidelity – like the one in the portrait of Eleonora Gonzaga – a tender and reassuring note in the scene; this carries on in the background, where two maid-servants are looking for clothes in a rich bridal chest, in a fading sunset.

The recent restoration has recovered Titian's typical colour scheme, highlighting the detail of fabric, of flesh tones, and even the small pearl shining on the ear of the young bride.

Awaited impatiently by Duke Guidubaldo della Rovere, the painting was to serve as an instructive "model" for Giulia Varano, the Duke's extremely young bride.

14

TITIAN
Portrait of Eleonora Gonzaga della Rovere

In this portrait painted between 1535 and 1538, the Duchess of Urbino appears in a setting made more intimate by the details of her little dog and a rare gilded clock, indicative of Eleonora's high rank. This portrait, like that of her husband Francesco Maria della Rovere, displayed in the same room, was known to art lovers even before being consigned to its owners. It was described in a letter dated November 7th 1537 by the poet Pietro Aretino, who greatly admired Titian for his skill in rendering his subjects even more lifelike than in nature, and interpreting through the brush the innermost secrets of the human soul as the writer should do with his pen. "I strive to depict the nature of others with the same liveliness with which the admirable Titian has portrayed that face", wrote Aretino. In a sonnet dedicated to Eleonora's portrait Aretino acclaims "the union of colours that Titian's style has diffused" and remarks on the virtues of the Duchess, clearly recognisable thanks to the artist's skill: her "harmony", "kind spirit", "honesty" and "modesty". In the fusion of art and painting (*ut pictura poesis*) the most noble characteristics are exalted according to the currently fashionable concept of *decorum*.

Room 29 ❖ Dosso and Parmigianino
Room 30 ❖ Cabinet of Emilian 16ᵗʰ century Painting

These two rooms contain the works of masters from Northern Italy, many of them of Emilian background, who developed a multitude of artistic languages, often highly original. Still debatable is the identity of some of these artists, such as the so-called Friuliano friend of Dosso, a name which may in reality refer to more than one person. Outstanding figures are Dosso Dossi, active in Ferrara at the Este court and then in Pesaro and Bologna, and Parmigianino, the refined, sophisticated artist who worked first in Parma, then in Rome and Bologna.

The works

1. DOSSO DOSSI
*Apparition of the Virgin
to St. John the Baptist
and St. John
the Evangelist*
c. 1517
Oil on wood,
transferred to
canvas in the past
153x114
Dep. Inv. no. 7
Restored: 1994

2. DOSSO DOSSI
*Rest on the flight
into Egypt*
c. 1519-1525
Tempera on wood
52x42.6
Inv. 1890 no. 8382

3. AMICO ASPERTINI
Adoration of the shepherds
1515
Oil on wood
44.5x34
Inv. 1890 no. 3803

4. EMILIAN SCHOOL
Portrait of a Boy
16ᵗʰ century
Oil on wood
58x44
Inv. 1890 no. 896

5. PARMIGIANINO
*The St.Zacchariah Madonna
(Madonna with Child
and Saints)*
c. 1530-1533
Oil on wood
75.5x60
Inv. 1890 no. 1328
Restored: 1994

6. PARMIGIANINO
*The Madonna
of the Long Neck
(Madonna with Child,
Angels and St. Jerome)*
c. 1534-1539
Oil on wood
219x135
Palatina Inv. no. 230

7. PARMIGIANINO
Portrait of a Man
c. 1550
Oil on wood
88x68.5
Inv. 1890 no. 1623
Restored: 1994

8. DOSSO DOSSI
Portrait of a Warrior
c. 1517
Oil on canvas
86x70
Inv. 1890 no. 889
Restored: 1994

9. FRIULIAN FRIEND OF DOSSO
Allegory
Fourth decade of the 16ᵗʰ century
Oil on wood
189x95
Inv. 1890 no. 5390
Restored: 1996

**10. FRIULIAN FRIEND OF DOSSO
(ATTR.)** (below)
Portrait of a Woman
Third-fourth decade
of the 16ᵗʰ century
Oil on wood, 82x63
Inv. 1890 no. 9950
Work acquired by Rodolfo
Siviero (formerly in the
Contini Bonacossi Collection)

**11. FRIULIAN FRIEND OF DOSSO
(ALSO ATTR. TO ALESSANDRO
OLIVERIO)** (above)
Portrait of a Man
(formerly thought to
be a *Self-portrait* by Sodoma)
First thirty years of the 16ᵗʰ century
Oil on canvas
78x60
Inv. 1890 no. 1688
Restored: 1996

12. DOSSO DOSSI
Witch-craft or
The Allegory of Hercules
c. 1535-1538
Oil on canvas
145x144
Inv. Palatina no. 148

13. GAROFALO
*Adoration
of the shepherds*
c. 1550
Oil on wood
37x47
San Marco and Cenacoli Inv. no. 82

14. GAROFALO
Annunciation
First half of the 16ᵗʰ century
Oil on wood
55.2x76
Inv. 1890 no. 1365

15. GAROFALO
St. Jerome
First half of the 16ᵗʰ century
Oil on wood
50x36
Inv. 1890 no. 6253
Restored: 1990

16. LUDOVICO MAZZOLINO
Adoration of the shepherds
c. 1520-1524
Oil on wood
79.5x60.5
Inv. 1890 no. 1352

17. LUDOVICO MAZZOLINO
*Madonna with Child
and Saints*
c. 1522-1523
Oil on wood
29.5x22.8
Inv. 1890 no. 1347
Restored: 1995

18. LUDOVICO MAZZOLINO
Circumcision
1526
Oil on curved
wood
40x29
Inv. 1890 no. 1355

19. LUDOVICO MAZZOLINO
Slaughter of the Innocents
c. 1525
Oil on wood
49x59
Inv. 1890 no. 1350

Room 29

Room 30

5

PARMIGIANINO
The St. Zacchariah Madonna
(Madonna with Child and Saints)

Painted in Bologna, possibly for Bonifacio Gozzadini, the panel shows the half-length figure of St. Zacchariah in the foreground, in a three-quarter pose, carrying a large open book. In front of him the Madonna sits and smiles, with the Child being embraced by a semi-nude infant St. John who is portrayed as a cupid. Behind this group is a fine and sensual Mary Magdalen, holding her vase of ointment, her breast partially covered by her hair. A livid sky in the background hangs over the mountains; distant cities reminiscent of Roman times can also be made out, reinforced in the middle ground by ancient ruins and a classical building with a Greek inscription. The painting is dated to the period of the artist's stay in Bologna, who had left Rome in 1527 after a period of three years.

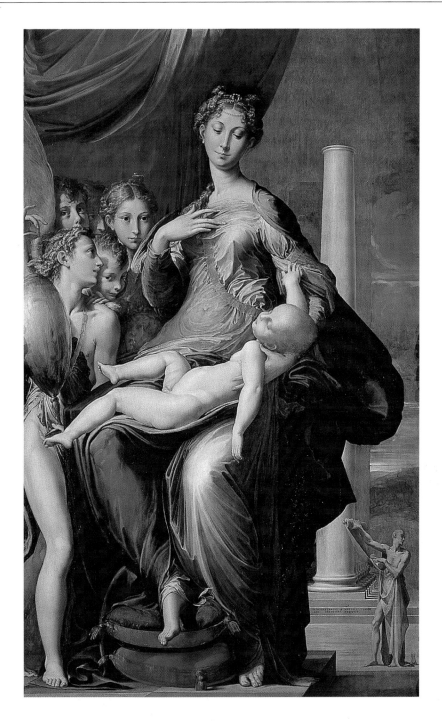

6

PARMIGIANINO
The Madonna of the Long Neck
(Madonna with Child, Angels and St. Jerome)

Painted for the Servi church in Parma. The inscription on the step beneath the column shows that this work remained unfinished, and in fact the painting was found in the artist's studio at his death at the age of thirty-seven in 1540. On the right side of the painting, famous for the refined, exaggerated length of its figures, there remains only the foot of a saint who was obviously to be painted alongside Jerome, depicted holding a scroll.

12 DOSSO DOSSI
Witch-craft or *Allegory of Hercules*

Acquired in Siena in 1665 for Cardinal Leopoldo, this is the masterpiece of the late period of Dossi's career, which began in 1514 at the Ferrara court and later moved to other cities. The meaning of the unusual subject matter is still doubtful. It is described in Cardinal Leopoldo's inventory as "the painting with portraits of the clowns of the Dukes of Ferrara". Rich in allusions and marked by a satirical note in the twisted faces, almost caricatures, it was perhaps dedicated to Ercole d'Este, the Duke of Ferrara.

19

LUDOVICO MAZZOLINO
Slaughter of the Innocents

This crowded and lively composition is a replica by the artist of the small panel now in the Doria Pamphilj Gallery in Rome (c. 1521); it dates to Mazzolino's mature period.

The rather mannered scene takes place against the background of a loggia which opens to the right onto a nordic-style landscape. Mazzolino was active in Ferrara from 1504, when he was commissioned by Ercole d'Este for a series of fresco decorations in the church of Santa Maria degli Angeli. These frescoes were lost in a fire in 1604. The artist is open to the new Venetian "colourism" and particularly to Giorgione. His work is also influenced by northern painting, mainly that of Dürer, a painter studied by many Italian artists thanks to the wide circulation of his etchings. Mazzolino's style is however marked by a "capricious" and bizarre imagination that fitted in well with the eclectic culture of a city like Ferrara.

In this small room are other paintings by the same master, all in the small dimensions through which Ludovico Mazzolino best expressed his talent.

Room 31 ❖ Veronese
Room 32 ❖ Bassano and Tintoretto

These two rooms, previously arranged differently, now contain numerous examples of late Veneto Mannerism, arriving almost at the threshold of the 17th century. The first room is dedicated to the airy, spectacular, scenic effects of Veronese, while the second contains various works, mainly portraits, by the prolific Tintoretto and the last great Mannerists from the Veneto, Jacopo Bassano and his son Leandro, whose lively Concert *has recently been restored.*

The works

1. PAOLO VERONESE
The martyrdom of Saint Justine
c. 1570-1575
Oil on canvas; 103x113
Inv. 1890 no. 946
Restored: 1988

2. PAOLO VERONESE
Holy Family with Saint Catherine and the infant St. John
c. 1562-1565
Oil on canvas; 86x122
Inv. 1890 no. 1433
Restored: 1988

3. PAOLO VERONESE
Annunciation
c. 1556
Oil on canvas; 143x291
Inv. 1890 no. 899

4. PAOLO VERONESE (ATTR.) (below)
Madonna enthroned among Saints and donors
1548
Oil on canvas; 50x36
Inv. 1890 no. 1316

5. ANDREA MICHIELI KNOWN AS VICENTINO (above)
Visitation
Early 17th century
Oil on canvas; 54x45
Inv. 1890 no. 1392

6. PAOLO VERONESE (below)
St. Agatha crowned by Angels
Beginning of the ninth decade of the 16th century
Oil on wood
19x17
Inv. 1890 no. 1343

7. VENETIAN SCHOOL (above)
Portrait of a Man
Second half of the 16th century
Oil on canvas; 47x39
Inv. 1890 no. 897

8. PAOLO VERONESE (ATTR.)
Esther brought before Ahasuerus
Sixth decade of the 16th century
Oil on canvas; 208x284
Inv. 1890 no. 912
Restored: 1996

9. BRUSASORCI
Bathsheba at her bath
c. 1550
Oil on canvas; 91x98
Inv. 1890 no. 953

10. BATTISTA FRANCO (below)
Going to Calvary
1552
Oil on canvas; 115x118
Inv. 1890 no. 9490
Restored: 1994

11. JACOPO BASSANO (above)
Judas and Tamar
Second half of the 16th century
Oil on canvas; 40x95
Inv. 1890 no. 927

12. PARIS BORDON (below)
Portrait of a Man
c. 1550
Oil on canvas; 131x105
Inv. 1890 no. 929
Restored: 1994

13. JACOPO BASSANO (above)
Two hunting dogs
c. 1560
Oil on canvas; 85x126
Inv. 1890 no. 965

14. GIAN PAOLO PACE
Portrait of Giovanni dalle Bande Nere
1545
Oil on canvas; 97x89
Inv. 1890 no. 934
Restored: 1996

15. PARIS BORDON (below)
Portrait of a Man with fur collar
c. 1530-1535
Oil on canvas; 107x83
Inv. 1890 no. 907
Restored: 1995

16. JACOPO BASSANO (above)
Announcement to the shepherds
Second half of the 16th century
Oil on canvas; 40x96
Inv. 1890 no. 920

17. JACOPO TINTORETTO (above)
Christ at the Samaritan woman's well
(from the organ of San Benedetto in Venice)
c. 1578
Oil on canvas; 116x93
Inv. 1890 no. 3497

18. JACOPO TINTORETTO
Leda and the Swan
c. 1550-1560
Oil on canvas; 167x221
Inv. 1890 no. 3084
Restored: 1994

19. VENETIAN SCHOOL (FORMERLY ATTR. TO JACOPO OR LEANDRO BASSANO)
Portrait of an Artist
End of the 16th century
Oil on canvas
110x88
Inv. 1890 no. 969

20. LEANDRO BASSANO
The Concert
c. 1590
Oil on canvas; 114x178
Inv. 1890 no. 915
Restored: 1998

21. JACOPO TINTORETTO AND WORKSHOP
Portrait of a Venetian admiral
c. 1570
Oil on canvas; 127x99
Inv. 1890 no. 921
Restored: 2000

22. JACOPO TINTORETTO
Adam and Eve before the Eternal
c. 1550-1553
Oil on canvas; 90x110
Inv. 1890 no. 8428

23. JACOPO TINTORETTO
Portrait of Jacopo Sansovino
c. 1566
Oil on canvas; 70x65.5
Inv. 1890 no. 957

24. JACOPO TINTORETTO (below)
Portrait of a Man with a red beard
1545
Oil on canvas; 52.5x45.5
Inv. 1890 no. 924
Restored: 1994

25. JACOPO TINTORETTO (above)
Portrait of a Man
Signed and dated 1546
Oil on wood; 30x22
Inv. 1890 no. 1387

26. JACOPO TINTORETTO (ATTR.)
Portrait of a Gentleman
c. 1550-1551
Oil on canvas; 154x131
Inv. 1890 no. 9951
Restored: 1994
Work acquired by Rodolfo Siviero

27. JACOPO TINTORETTO (above)
The Samaritan woman at the well
(from the organ of San Benedetto in Venice)
c. 1578
Oil on canvas; 116x93
Inv. 1890 no. 3498

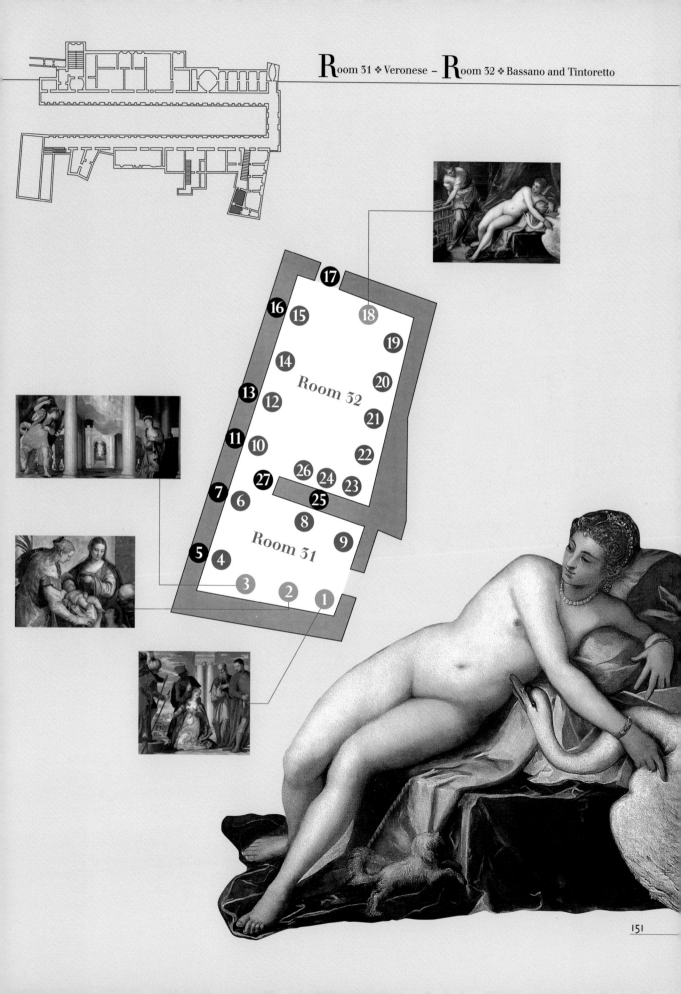

Room 32

Room 31

PAOLO VERONESE
The martyrdom of Saint Justine

This canvas by Veronese was formerly part of the Canonici di Ferrara Collection (1632), and later belonged to Paolo del Sera, an intermediary in Venice for Cardinal Leopoldo de' Medici who then bought it from him around 1654.

The subject of the painting is the same as that of a great and more animated altarpiece possibly executed by Paolo Veronese together with his brother for the Basilica of Santa Giustina in Padua (c. 1574), for which a preparatory drawing exists (Chatsworth, collection of the Duke of Devonshire). Veronese, who in 1573 underwent a trial for taking too much liberty with his depiction of holy themes, was a master at creating spectacular scenes filled with light.

Further canvases of his displayed in this room come from Cardinal Leopoldo's collections: an airy, monumental *Annunciation* (Inv. no. 899) and the *Holy Family* from Widmann House (Inv. no. 1433), a painting dominated by the imposing blonde figure of Saint Catherine.

PAOLO VERONESE
*Holy Family with Saint Catherine
and the infant St. John*

Transferred to the Uffizi in 1798, this painting was in Venice at the Widmann residence in 1648. This important family of Carinthian origin owned a sumptuous palace near San Canciano, which was later decorated with a series of large canvases by the Venetian painter Gregorio Lazzarini. This work by Veronese, highly esteemed by such a fine 17th century connoisseur as Marco Boschini, is one of the most important from the painter's late maturity. Based on stylistic similarities it can be dated close to the so-called *San Zaccaria Altarpiece*, another famous painting completed in 1564,

which once hung in the sacristy of the church from which it takes its name and is now in the Accademia Galleries in Venice. While in the *St. Zacchariah Altarpiece* the Holy Family is portrayed in a vertical configuration, viewed foreshortened within the setting of a chapel, the figures in the Florence painting appear in three-quarter view. This highly effective close-up can be appreciated even more today, now that restoration has restored luminosity to the faces and clothing, revealing again the original light background, obscured for years by repainting.

153

PAOLO VERONESE
Annunciation

Lit up by pale golden flashes of light, the holy event is set in a scenario reminiscent of the architecture of Palladio and Sansovino. Between the columns, the cloud of the Holy Spirit "breaks up" the composition which, continuing toward the background, reveals a glimpse of a magnificent landscape traversed by a shady path evocative of silence and meditation. The painting, transferred to the Uffizi in 1789, originally belonged to the Venetian collection of Paolo del Sera, from whom Cardinal Leopoldo de' Medici bought it in 1654. Although its autography has at times been questioned, it is now believed to be a youthful work, datable around 1556, and comparable for its similar but not identical scheme to a painting in the Civic Museum of Padua attributed to Battista Zelotti, a contemporary of Veronese who worked with him in Antonio Badile's workshop.

JACOPO TINTORETTO
Leda and the Swan

This painting, donated to the Uffizi in 1893 by Arturo De Noè Walker it was listed, at the end of the 18th century in the collection of the Duke of Orléans in Paris, then in that of the Duke of Bridgewater in London and in 1857 it was still in London, owned by P. Norton. In an interior embellished with pets (a parrot in an aviary, a cat staring threateningly at a caged duck, and a little dog who is perhaps jealous of the swan), the painting shows the mythical, sensual Leda, dressed only in pearls, caressing Jove, who has transformed himself into a swan to seduce her. Recent restorations has clarified that the presence of the maidservant is not arbitrary as far as its prototype is concerned (Inv. no. 9946, formerly in the Contini Bonacossi Collection, acquired after the war by Rodolfo Siviero, and transferred to the Uffizi in 1989). In the latter work, painted about ten years earlier and also recently restored, the posturing servant girl was originally present, disappearing later because of a cut in the canvas.

Room 33 ❖ Corridor of the 16ᵗʰ century

The corridor between the Bassano and Tintoretto Room and that of the 16ᵗʰ century Lombard painters was enlarged and modernized in 1999 according to more up-to-date museum criteria. It now documents, with a consistent core of works of small format, many of them painted on copper, the refined Mannerist style that flourished in the European courts of the second half of the 16ᵗʰ century. Outstanding among the Spanish, French and Flemish artists are El Greco, François Clouet and Frans Floris; among the Italians, Scarsellino, Lavinia Fontana and Luca Cambiaso. The most prolific Florentine artists active at the Medici court are also represented: Giorgio Vasari, Agnolo Bronzino, Alessandro Allori and Jacopo Zucchi, all of whom had worked on the Studiolo of Francesco I in Palazzo Vecchio around 1570.

The works

1. **EL GRECO**
   Saints John the Evangelist and Francis
   c. 1600
   Oil on canvas; 110x86
   Inv. 1890 no. 9493

2. **LUIS DE MORALES**
   Christ carrying the Cross
   c. 1550-1560
   Oil on wood; 59.5x56
   Inv. 1890 no. 3112

3. **ALONSO SÁNCHEZ COELLO**
   Portrait of Elisabeth of Valois
   c. 1570
   Oil on canvas; 51.5x44.5
   Inv. 1890 no. 9955
   Formerly Contini Bonacossi
   Collection, work acquired
   in Germany on 1948

4. **FRANS FLORIS**
   Susannah and the Elders
   c. 1562-1563
   Oil on wood; 150x210
   Inv. San Marco and Cenacoli no. 24

5. **FRENCH PAINTER?**
   Man in armor
   Mid 16ᵗʰ century
   Oil on wood; 71.5x58
   Inv. 1890 no. 1504

6. **FRENCH PAINTER**
   Portrait of Christine of Lorraine
   1588
   Oil on wood; 39.5x32.5
   Inv. 1890 no. 4338

7. **FRANÇOIS CLOUET**
   François I of France on horseback
   c. 1540
   Tempera on wood; 27.5x22.5
   Inv. 1890 no. 987

8. **SCHOOL OF FONTAINEBLEAU**
   Two Women bathing
   Last quarter of the 16ᵗʰ century
   Oil on wood; 129x97
   Inv. 1890 no. 9958. Work acquired
   by Rodolfo Siviero in 1948

9. **JOACHIM BEUCKELAER**
   Pilat showing Jesus to the people
   1566
   Oil on wood; 110x140
   Inv. 1890 no. 2215
   Restored: 1985

10. **GIORGIO VASARI**
    Adoration of the shepherds
    c. 1546
    Tempera on wood; 90x67
    Inv. 1890 no. 9449

11. **AGNOLO BRONZINO**
    Christ deposed
    c. 1565-1570
    Oil on copper; 42x30
    Inv. 1890 no. 1554

12. **GIORGIO VASARI (FORMERLY ATTR. TO CECCHINO SALVIATI)**
    Artemisia weeping Mausolus
    c. 1545
    Oil on wood; 35x24.5
    Inv. 1890 no. 1528

13. **GIORGIO VASARI**
    Vulcan's Forge
    c. 1564
    Oil on copper; 38x28
    Inv. 1890 no. 1558
    Restored: 1997

14. **AGNOLO BRONZINO**
    Allegory of Happiness
    c. 1567
    Oil on copper; 40x30
    Inv. 1890 no. 1543

15. **ALESSANDRO ALLORI**
    Hercules crowned by the Muses
    c. 1570
    Oil on copper; 39x29
    Inv. 1890 no. 1544

16. **ALESSANDRO ALLORI**
    Venus and Cupid
    16ᵗʰ century
    Oil on wood; 29x38
    Inv. 1890 no. 1512

17. **FRANCESCO MORANDINI KNOWN AS POPPI**
    The three Graces
    16ᵗʰ century
    Oil on copper; 30x25
    Inv. 1890 no. 1471

18. **JACOPO ZUCCHI**
    Rest on the flyght into Egypt
    Second half of the 16ᵗʰ century
    Oil on copper; 51x39
    Inv. 1890 no. 6208

19. **JACOPO ZUCCHI**
    The Iron Age
    (or *The Age of Jupiter*)
    c. 1577
    Oil on copper; 50x39
    Inv. 1890 no. 1509

20. **JACOPO ZUCCHI**
    The Silver Age
    c. 1576-1581
    Oil on wood; 50x39
    Inv. 1890 no. 1506
    Restored: 1997

21. **JACOPO ZUCCHI**
    The Golden Age
    c. 1576-1581
    Oil on wood; 50x39
    Inv. 1890 no. 1548
    Restored: 1997

22. **LUCA CAMBIASO**
    Madonna and Child
    c. 1570
    Oil on canvas; 74.3x59.5
    Inv. 1890 no. 776

23. **VENTURA MAZZA (?)**
    Annunciation
    Second half of the 16ᵗʰ century
    (from Federico Barocci)
    Oil on wood; 51x37
    Inv. San Marco
    and Cenacoli no. 64

24. **DOMENICO CAMPAGNOLA (ATTR.)**
    Portrait of a Man
    16ᵗʰ century
    Oil on wood; 62x45.5
    Inv. 1890 no. 895

25. **SCARSELLINO**
    The Judgement of Paris
    c. 1590
    Oil on copper; 51x73.5
    Inv. 1890 no. 1382

26. **FEDERICO BAROCCI**
    Portrait of a Young girl
    c. 1570-1575
    Oil on paper; 45x33
    Inv. 1890 no. 765

27. **FEDERICO BAROCCI**
    Self-portrait
    Late of the 16ᵗʰ century
    Oil on canvas; 34x27
    Inv. 1890 no. 1848

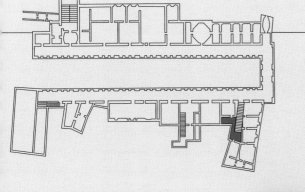

28. Orazio Samacchini (attr.)
Susannah at the bath
c. 1570-1575
Oil on wood; 34.5x29
Inv. 1890 no. 1511

29. Orazio Samacchini
Joseph and Potiphar's wife
c. 1570-1575
Oil on wood; 34x29
Inv. 1890 no. 1515

30. Niccolò dell'Abate
Portrait of a Young man
c. 1540
Oil on wood; 47x41
Inv. 1890 no. 1377

31. Denijs Calvaert
Assumption of Mary
1602
Oil on copper; 58x45
Inv. 1890 no. 1338

32. Lavinia Fontana
*Apparition of Jesus
to the Magdalene*
Signed and dated 1581
Oil on canvas; 80x65.5
Inv. 1890 no. 1383
Restored: 1994

**33. Herri Met de Bles
known as Civetta**
The Copper mines
First half of the 16th century
Oil on wood; 83x114
Inv. 1890 no. 1051

34. Santi di Tito
Madonna with Child and Saints
Second half of the 16th century
Oil on wood; 100x75
Inv. 1890 no. 3902

35. Cigoli
Flight into Egypt
Late 16th century
Oil on copper; 50x35
Inv. 1890 no. 1053

**36. Mirabello Cavalori (attr.)
(traditionally attributed to
Pontormo, in collaboration
with Bronzino)**
*Madonna and Child with two
Angels, Saints Francis and Jerome*
c. 1524 (if Pontormo),
c. 1565 (if Cavalori)
Oil on wood; 73x61
Inv. 1890 no. 1558

37. Jacopo Ligozzi
The Sacrifice of Isaac
c. 1596
Oil on wood; 51x37.5
Inv. 1890 no. 1337

38. Andrea Boscoli
St. Sebastian
Early 17th century
Oil on wood; 45.5x26
Inv. 1890 no. 6204

39. Andrea Boscoli
Pyramus and Thisbe
Early 17th century
Oil on wood; w. m.
Inv. 1890 no. 10033
Restored: 1999

40. Florentine painter
Ulysses on Circe's Island
c. 1570-1580
Oil on wood; 130x183
Inv. 1890 no. 9934
Work acquired by Rodolfo Siviero

41. Maso da San Friano
The Fall of Icarus
1570
Oil on wood; 56x41
Inv. 1890 no. 6233
Restored: 1994

42. Artist near to Jacopo Ligozzi
The Fortune
Late 16th century
Oil on wood; 46x26
Inv. 1890 no. 8023

43. Alessandro Allori
Portrait of Bianca Cappello
Last quarter of the 16th century
Oil on copper; 37x27
Inv. 1890 no. 1514. Restored: 1997

44. Alessandro Allori
Sacrifice of Isaac
1601
Oil on wood; 94x131
Inv. 1890 no. 1553

45. Alessandro Allori (attr.)
Portrait of Ludovico Capponi?
1585-1590. Oil on wood; 45x36
Inv. 1890 no. 763

46. Alessandro Allori
St. Peter walking on the water
1596? Oil on copper; 47x40
Inv. 1890 no. 1549

**47. Jacopo Chimenti
know as Empoli**
Drunkenness of Noah
c. 1594
Oil on copper; 31x25
Inv. 1890 no. 1531

**48. Jacopo Chimenti
know as Empoli**
Sacrifice of Isaac
c. 1594
Oil on copper; 32x25
Inv. 1890 n. 1463

7

FRANÇOIS CLOUET
François I of France on horseback

This small court portrait arrived in Florence in 1589 when Christine of Lorraine, wife of Ferdinando I, inherited numerous works of art from her grandmother Caterina de' Medici, Queen of France. Equestrian portraits of French kings were often executed in miniature, and Clouet, court painter after his father Jean, was expert in this format.

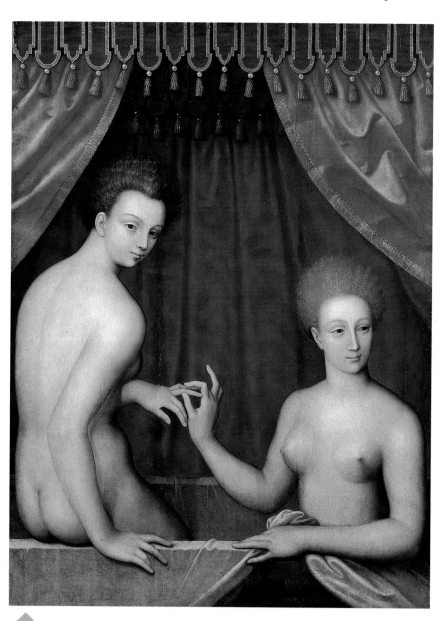

8

SCHOOL OF FONTAINEBLEAU
Two Women bathing

It is not known who the two women in this painting are. Portrayed in different versions, they are generally identified as Gabrielle d'Estrées (1571-1599), lover of Henri IV, and her sister, the Duchess of Villars. They coincide with the standards of ideal beauty expressed by 16th century poetry, where white, yellow, and red were the favourite colours.

13

GIORGIO VASARI
Vulcan's Forge

Perhaps originally in the Tribune, this small copper plate depicts the forge of Vulcan, god of subterranean fires. Symbol of genius, Vulcan is intent on chiselling a shield showing Capricorn, the astrological sign of Francesco I de' Medici, and Aries, the ancestor of his father, Cosimo, holding up the world. At the upper left are the Three Graces, emblems of the Art of Drawing, modelling for four nude artists.

The composition, rich in figures and symbolic allusions, also gives an idea of the 16th century artist's workshop.

20-21

JACOPO ZUCCHI
The Silver Age (left)
The Golden Age (right)

The two paintings were in the Guardaroba of Cardinal Ferdinando de' Medici, where they may have been inserted in a piece of furniture or have been used as portrait covers. They have been linked to drawings (in the Louvre) by Vasari, Zucchi's master, with whom he collaborated in decorating the Studiolo in Palazzo Vecchio. Typical of the taste of late Mannerism, these two small paintings, rich in symbols and allegorical meaning, re-evoke the mythical Ages of the world. *The Golden Age* in particular seems inspired by the aria "O begli anni dell'oro" which had been sung at the wedding of Cosimo and Eleonora of Toledo in 1539.

Room 34 ❖ Lombard Painting of the 16ᵗʰ century

Known as the Porcelain Room in the mid-16ᵗʰ century, this hall was renamed the "second chamber of painters" in 1779 when a series of self-portraits was placed here in a new arrangement. Already for some time, in fact, a part of the Medicean collection of self-portraits had been exhibited in the preceding room, now dedicated to the sophisticated world of the 16ᵗʰ century European courts. Up to a few years ago this room was consecrated to Veronese, but the recent arrangement has brought here some masterpieces of 16ᵗʰ century Lombard painting: a culture of great versatility and highly varying languages with outstanding personalities such as Lorenzo Lotto, a highly inventive painter born in Venice but working in many different localities, who ended his life in Loreto; the Brescian Savoldo – also active in numerous cities of northern Italy as well as in Florence – influenced by Venetian colouristic effects and particularly attentive to research in lighting; and lastly the great portrait painter from Bergamo Giovan Battista Moroni, sensitive interpreter of his patrons' physiological features.

The works

1. **BERNARDINO LICINIO (ATTR.)**
Nude
c. 1530
Oil on canvas; 80.5x154
Inv. 1890 no. 9943
Work acquired by Rodolfo Siviero

2. **SEBASTIANO FLORIGERIO**
Portrait of Raffaele Grassi
First half of the 16ᵗʰ century
Oil on canvas
127x103
Inv. 1890 no. 894

3. **BERNARDINO CAMPI
(FORMERLY ATTR. TO
GIROLAMO MUZIANO)**
Portrait of a Man
Second half of the 16ᵗʰ century
Oil on canvas, 75x60
Inv. 1890 no. 891
Restored: 2000

4. **GIOVAN BATTISTA MORONI**
*Portrait of the poet
Giovanni Antonio Pantera*
c. 1550-1560
Oil on canvas, 81x63
Inv. 1890 no. 941
Restored: 2001

5. **GIOVAN BATTISTA MORONI**
Portrait of Pietro Secco Suardo
1563
Oil on canvas
183x104
Inv. 1890 no. 906

6. **GIOVAN BATTISTA MORONI**
Portrait of a Learned man
End of the sixth decade
of the 16ᵗʰ century
Oil on canvas, 69x61
Inv. 1890 no. 933
Restored: 2000

7. **PAINTER FROM NORTHERN ITALY**
*Portrait (presumed)
of Teofilo Folengo*
First half of the 16ᵗʰ century
Oil on wood
83x79
Inv. 1890 no. 791

8. **LORENZO LOTTO**
*Holy Family with Sts. Jerome,
Anne and Giovacchino*
Signed and dated 1534
Oil on canvas
69x87.5
Inv. 1890 no. 893

9. **GIOVAN GEROLAMO SAVOLDO**
Transfiguration
c. 1525-1535
Oil on wood, 139x126
Inv. 1890 no. 930
Restored: 1997

10. **LORENZO LOTTO**
The Chastity of Susannah
Signed and dated 1517
on the inner edge
of the bathing pool
Oil on wood
66x50
Inv. 1890 no. 9491

11. **LORENZO LOTTO**
Portrait of a Young man
c. 1505-1506
Oil on wood
28x22
Inv. 1890 no. 1481

12. **PAOLO PINO**
Portrait of a Gentleman
Signed and dated 1534
Oil on canvas
89x74
Inv. 1890 no. 968

13. **SOFONISBA ANGUISSOLA
(FORMERLY ATTR. TO
GIULIO CAMPI)**
*Portrait
of an Unknown man*
Second half
of the 16ᵗʰ century
Oil on canvas
72.5x58
Inv. 1890 no. 1796

14. **GIROLAMO FIGINO
(FORMERLY ATTR. TO
AURELIO LUINI)**
*Madonna and Child
with Saint Margaret
and Saint Magdalene*
16ᵗʰ century
Oil on wood
66x50
Inv. 1890 no. 788

15. **GIULIO CAMPI
(ATTR.)**
Guitar-player
c. 1530-1540
Oil on canvas
74x58
Inv. 1890 no. 958
Restored: 2002

16. **GIULIO CAMPI**
*Portrait
of Galeazzo Campi*
c. 1530-1540
Oil on canvas
78.5x62
Inv. 1890 no. 1628

17. **CAMILLO BOCCACCINO
(ATTR.)**
Head of an Old man
c. 1540
Paper on wood
57x40
Inv. 1890 no. 7103

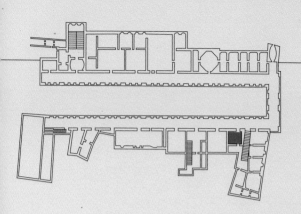

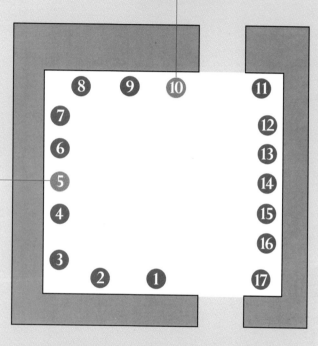

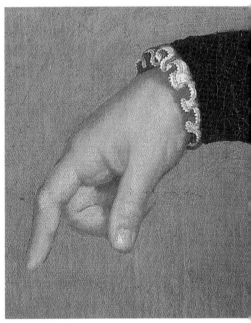

5

GIOVAN BATTISTA MORONI
Portrait of Pietro Secco Suardo

Famous for the psychological realism of his portraits, Moroni, a painter from Bergamo, portrays his countryman Pietro Secco Suardo, Ambassador of Venice from 1545. A few precise brush strokes render this essential interior: the deformed shadow on the square pavement and the window view. On a base stands the burning brazier, alluding to the family motto, taken from St. Luke's Gospel (12, 49): "How I wish it [the fire] were blazing already". The Latin words [NI]S[I] U[T] ARDE[AT] conceal in acrostic the nobleman's surname.

10

LORENZO LOTTO
The Chastity of Susannah

A man of culture, a wanderer and a loner, Lotto painted here the Biblical episode of Susannah being harassed while bathing by two old men whom she drives away. The traditional scene is viewed from above to show in the background, beyond the wall, two old men hidden in the branches of a tree spying on Susannah as she walks to the bath. On didactic scrolls, as if in anticipation of our modern comic strips, Susannah declares that she does not want to sin, while the old men accuse her of adultery with a young man.

Rooms 35-45 and New Rooms (First Floor)

The works

Room 35

1. CIGOLI
Deposition
1579-1580. Oil on wood; 320x220
Inv. 1890/7791. Restored: 1996

2. JACOPO CHIMENTI KNOW AS EMPOLI
Martyrdom of Saint Barbara
1605. Oil on canvas; 299x197. Inv. 1890/3174

3. BERNARDINO POCCETTI
*The Virgin appearing to the Saints
Nicholas of Bari and Bruno*
1595. Oil on canvas; 232x160. Inv. 1890/10081

4. CIGOLI
Stigmata of St. Francis
1596. Oil on wood; 248x174
Inv. 1890/3496. Restored: 1995

5. FEDERICO BAROCCI
Portrait of Ippolito della Rovere
c. 1602. Oil on canvas; 106.5x88.5. Inv. 1890/567

6. FEDERICO BAROCCI
Noli me tangere
c. 1590. Oil on canvas; 122x91
Inv. 1890/798. Restored: 2000

7. FEDERICO BAROCCI
Portrait of Francesco Maria II della Rovere
c. 1572. Oil on canvas; 113x93. Inv. 1890/1438

8. FEDERICO BAROCCI
Stigmata of St. Francis
After 1597. Oil on canvas; 126x98. Inv. 1890/790

9. FEDERICO BAROCCI
Madonna of the People
Signed and dated 1579. Oil on wood; 359x252
Inv. 1890/751. Restored: 1995

10. FEDERICO BAROCCI
*St Elisabeth's Family visits the Holy Family,
known as the 'Madonna of the Cat'*
1598 or 1605
Oil on canvas; 253x179
Inv. 1890/5375. Restored: 2002-2003

11. PASSIGNANO
St. Luke painting the Virgin
Late 16th-early 17th century
Oil on canvas; 525x250
Inv. 1890/8048. Restored: 1998

12. ALESSANDRO ALLORI
*Christ dead with the Virgin
and three Angels*
Signed and dated 1580
Oil on canvas; 253x181
Inv. 1890/5854. Restored: 1999

13. LUDOVICO BUTI
Assumption of the Virgin
c. 1600. Oil on canvas; 289x195
Inv. w. no. Restored: 1996

14. SANTI DI TITO
Bene scripsisti de me Thoma
1593. Oil on wood; 270x195
Inv. w. no. (in temporary storage)

Room 41

15. PIETER PAUL RUBENS AND WORKSHOP
Judith with the head of Holophernes
c. 1625. Oil on canvas; 115x89
Inv. 1890/9966. Restored: 1994
Work acquired by Rodolfo Siviero in 1948

16. ANTOON VAN DYCK
Portrait of Jean de Monfort
c. 1628. Oil on canvas; 123x86. Inv. 1890/1436

17. PIETER PAUL RUBENS AND WORKSHOP
Bacchus on a barrel
c. 1640. Oil on canvas; 152x118
Inv. 1890/796. Restored: 1993

18. JAN VAN DEN HOECKE
Hercules between Vice and Virtue
c. 1647-1651
Oil on canvas; 145x194. Inv. 1890/1442

**19. DANIEL SEGHERS
(AND JAN VAN DEN HOECKE?)**
*Garland of flowers with marble bust
of the Archduke Leopoldo Guglielmo*
Signed, formerly dated 1647?
(date no longer legible)
Oil on copper; 117x96. Inv. 1890/1085

20. SCHOOL OF ANTOON VAN DYCK
*Presumed portrait of the mother
of Justus Sustermans*
c. 1640-1650. Oil on canvas; 81x63. Inv. 1890/726

21. PIETER PAUL RUBENS
Battle (Henri IV at the Battle of Ivry)
c. 1627-1630. Oil on canvas; 367x693
Inv. 1890/722. Restored: 2000

22. SPANISH SCHOOL
Portrait of a Gentleman
17th century. Oil on canvas; 124x100. Inv. 1890/10024
(confiscated work by Rodolfo Siviero,
formerly in the Contini Bonacossi Collection)

23. DIEGO VELÁZQUEZ AND WORKSHOP
Self-portrait
c. 1645. Oil on canvas; 103.5x85.5
Inv. 1890/1707. Restored: 1987

24. ANTOON VAN DYCK
The Emperor Charles V on horseback
c. 1620. Oil on canvas; 191x123
Inv. 1890/1439. Restored: 1986

25. DIEGO VELÁZQUEZ AND WORKSHOP
Philip IV of Spain on horseback
c. 1645. Oil on canvas; 337x263
Inv. 1890/792. Restored: 1995

26. ANTOON VAN DYCK
*Portrait of Marguerite of Lorraine,
Duchess of Orléans*
c. 1634. Oil on canvas; 204x117
Inv. 1890/777. Restored: 1993

27. PIETER PAUL RUBENS
Portrait of Isabel Brandt
c. 1625. Oil on wood; 86x62. Inv. 1890/779

28. PIETER PAUL RUBENS
Self-portrait
1628. Oil on wood; 78x61. Inv. 1890/1890

29. PIETER PAUL RUBENS
*Triumph (Triumphal entry
of Henri IV in Paris)*
1627-1630. Oil on canvas; 380x692
Inv. 1890/729. Restored: 2000

30. JACOB JORDAENS (ATTR.)
Presumed portrait of the artist's mother
c. 1660. Oil on canvas; 68x50. Inv. 1890/3141

31. JUSTUS SUSTERMANS
Portrait of Galileo Galilei
1636. Oil on canvas; 66x56
Inv. 1890/745. Restored: 1999

32. JAN VAN DEN HOECKE
*Triumphal entry of the Prince
Ferdinand of Spain into Antwerp*
1634-1635
Oil on canvas; 405x328. Inv. 1890/5404

Room 43

33. SIGISMONDO COCCAPANI
Flute Player
c. 1630-1640
Oil on canvas; 84.5x76. Inv. 1890/6034

34. ANNIBALE CARRACCI
Self-portrait on profile
1590-1600
Oil on canvas; 45.4x37.9. Inv. 1890/1797

35. ANNIBALE CARRACCI
Man with a monkey
1590-1591
Oil on canvas; 68x58.3. Inv. 1890/799

36. ANNIBALE CARRACCI
Venus, a Satyr and two Cupids
c. 1588
Oil on canvas; 112x142. Inv. 1890/1452

37. MATTIA PRETI
Vanitas
c. 1650-1670
Oil on canvas; 93.5x65. Inv. 1890/9283

38. GUERCINO
Sibyl
1644
Oil on canvas; 114x95. Inv. 1890/1430

39. DOMENICHINO
Portrait of Cardenal Agucchi
1605
Oil on canvas; 142x112. Inv. 1890/1428

40. DOMENICO FETI
Ecce Homo
Early 17th century
Oil on canvas; 136x112. Inv. 1890/6279

41. BERNARDO STROZZI
The Tribute of Money
c. 1630
Oil on canvas; 158x225. Inv. 1890/808

42. CLAUDE LORRAIN
Port with Villa Medici
1637. Oil on canvas; 102x133.
Inv. 1890/1096. Restored: 1994

Room 44

43. FRANS VAN MIERIS THE ELDER
Two Old people at table
c. 1655-1660
Oil on wood; 36x31.5. Inv. 1890/1267

44. GERRIT BERCKHEYDE
Self-portrait
1675. Oil on wood; 35x30. Inv. 1890/1775

45. GABRIEL METSU
Woman playing a lute
c. 1660-1665
Oil on wood; 31x27.5. Inv. 1890/1238

46. HENDRICK POT
The Miser
c. 1640-1650
Oil on wood; 36x32.7. Inv. 1890/1284

47. ABRAHAM MIGNON
Still-Life
Second half of the 17th century
Oil on wood; 36.5x47.5. Inv. 1890/1115

48. PIETER CODDE
Conversation
17th century
Oil on wood; 27x20.5. Inv. 1890/8446

49. GERRIT DOU
The hotcakes seller
c. 1650-1655
Oil on wood; 44x34. Inv. 1890/1246

50. JAN VAN DER HEYDEN
*View of the Royal Palace
in Amsterdam*
1667
Oil on canvas; 85x92. Inv. 1890/1211

51. ADRIAEN VAN DER WERFF
Adoration of the shepherds
1703
Oil on wood; 53x36. Inv. 1890/1313

52. PIETER CODDE
Concert
17th century
Oil on wood; 27x20.5. Inv. 1890/8445

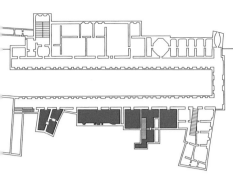

53. GERRIT BERCKHEYDE
The Groote Markt in Haarlem
1693
Oil on canvas; 54x64. Inv. 1890/1219

54. REMBRANDT
Self-portrait as a Young man
c. 1634. Oil on wood; 62.5x54
Inv. 1890/3890. Restored: 2002

55. REMBRANDT
Portrait of an Old man ("The Rabbi")
1665
Oil on canvas; 104x86. Inv. 1890/8435

56. REMBRANDT
Self-portrait
c. 1664. Oil on canvas; 74x55. Inv. 1890/1871

57. HERMAN VAN SWANEVELT
(FORMERLY ATTR. TO JAN BOTH)
Landscape
c. 1640
Oil on canvas; 52x66. Inv. 1890/1310

58. MICHIEL VAN MIEREVELD
Portrait of a Gentleman
c. 1615-1625
Oil on wood; 106x73. Inv. 1890/728

59. MICHIEL VAN MIEREVELD
Portrait of a Lady
c. 1615-1625
Oil on wood; 106x73. Inv. 1890/725

60. JACOB VAN RUYSDAEL
Landscape with shepherds and peasants
c. 1660-1670
Oil on canvas; 52x60. Inv. 1890/1201

61. HERCULES PIETERSZ SEGHERS
Mountain landscape
c. 1620-1630
Canvas glued to wood ; 55x99. Inv. 1890/1303

Room 45

62. JEAN BAPTISTE-SIMÉON CHARDIN
Girl with the shuttlecock
c. 1741. Oil on canvas; 82x66. Inv. 1890/9274

63. JEAN BAPTISTE-SIMÉON CHARDIN
Boy with a cards castle
c. 1740. Oil on canvas; 82x66. Inv. 1890/9273

64. JEAN-MARC NATTIER
Marie Zephirine of France
1751. Oil on canvas; 70x82. Inv. Dep. 22

65. JEAN-ETIENNE LIOTARD
*Presumed portrait of Marie Adelaide
of France dressed in Turkish costume*
1753. Oil on canvas; 50x56. Inv. Dep. no. 47

66. FRANCISCO DE GOYA Y LUCIENTES
The Countess of Chinchón
c. 1801
Oil on canvas; 220x140. Inv. 1890/9484

67. FRANCISCO DE GOYA Y LUCIENTES
*Maria Teresa de Vallabriga
on horseback*
1783. Oil on canvas; 82.5x61.7 Inv. 1890/9485

68. GIUSEPPE MARIA CRESPI
The flea
1710. Oil on copper; 46.5x34
Inv. 1890/1408. Restored: 1993

69. GIUSEPPE MARIA CRESPI
Portrait of the painter Giovanni Sorbi
c. 1715-1720. Oil on canvas; 74x58
Inv. 1890/2058. Restored: 1993

70. GIUSEPPE MARIA CRESPI
Cupid and Psyche
c. 1709. Oil on canvas; 130x215
Inv. 1890/5443. Restored: 1990

71. ALESSANDRO MAGNASCO
Gipsies' meal
c. 1710. Oil on canvas; 56x71. Inv. 1890/8470

72. GIOVANNI PAOLO PANNINI
*Architectonic "Capriccio"
("The Bethesda pool")*
c. 1740. Oil on canvas; 98x132
Inv. 1890/10040. Work donated in 1994

73. ALESSANDRO LONGHI
Portrait of a Lady
c. 1770. Oil on canvas; 100x80. Inv. 1890/3573

74. PIETRO LONGHI
The confession
c. 1755. Oil on canvas; 57x43. Inv. 1890/9275

75. CANALETTO (ATTR.)
Caprice of lagoon with tomb
c. 1755. Oil on canvas; 44.5x60. Inv. 1890/3554

76. CANALETTO (ATTR.)
Caprice of lagoon with house and bell tower
c. 1755. Oil on canvas; 44.5x60. Inv. 1890/3555

77. CANALETTO
View of the Ducal Palace in Venice
Before 1755. Oil on canvas; 51x83
Inv. 1890/1554. Restored: 2001

78. CANALETTO
View of the Canal Grande in Venice
c. 1730. Oil on canvas; 45x73. Inv. 1890/1518

79. FRANCESCO GUARDI
Caprice with bridges over a canal
c. 1780. Oil on canvas; 30x53. Inv. 1890/3559

80. FRANCESCO GUARDI
Caprice with arch and quay
c. 1780. Oil on canvas; 30x53. Inv. 1890/3558

81. ALESSANDRO LONGHI
Portrait of a judge
1776. Oil on canvas; 94x78. Inv. 1890/9181

82. GIAMBATTISTA TIEPOLO
Rinaldo abandons Armida
c. 1750. Oil on canvas; 70x132. Inv. 1890/9992
Work acquired by Rodolfo Siviero in 1954

83. GIAMBATTISTA TIEPOLO
*Rinaldo mirrors himself
in the Ubaldo's shield*
c. 1750. Oil on canvas; 69x132. Inv. 1890/9991
Work acquired by Rodolfo Siviero in 1954

84. ROSALBA CARRIERA
*Portrait of Felicita Sartori
in Turkish costume*
c. 1730-1740. Pastels on canvas; 70x55
Inv. 1890/9988.Formerly in the Contini Bonacossi
Collection, work acquired by Rodolfo Siviero in 1953

New Rooms (First Floor)

85. ARTEMISIA GENTILESCHI
Saint Catherine of Alexandria
c. 1618-1619. Oil on canvas; 77x62
Inv. 1890/8032. Restored: 1995-1994

86. CARAVAGGESQUE PAINTER
Double portrait
Third decade of the 17th century
Oil on canvas; 50x60. Inv. 1890/4235

87. ARTEMISIA GENTILESCHI
Judith and Holofernes
c. 1620-1621. Oil on canvas; 199x162.5
Inv. 1890/1567. Restored: 1994-1995

88. CARAVAGGIO
Sacrifice of Isaac
c. 1603. Oil on canvas; 104x135. Inv. 1890/4659

89. CARAVAGGIO
Medusa
c. 1595-1598
Oil on wood covered with canvas; diam. 55
Inv. 1890/1351. Restored: 2002

90. BATTISTELLO
*Salome with the Head
of St John the Baptist*
c. 1615-1620. Oil on canvas; 132x156
Inv. Dep. 30. Restored 1993

91. CARAVAGGIO
The Adolescent Bacchus
c. 1598.Oil on canvas; 95x85. Inv. 1890/5512

92. CARAVAGGESQUE PAINTER
*Copy of the "Concert"
by Bartolomeo Manfredi*
c. 1650. Oil on canvas; 150x190. Inv. 1890/6529

93. BARTOLOMEO MANFREDI
Tribute to Caesar
1618-1620. Oil on canvas; 130x191
Inv. 1890/778. Restored 1993-1994

94. BARTOLOMEO MANFREDI
Christ Mocked
1618-1620. Oil on canvas; 122x147
Inv. Oggetti d'arte 1317

95. BARTOLOMEO MANFREDI
Disputation with the Doctors
1618-1620. Oil on canvas; 129.5x190
Inv. 1890/767. Restored 1993-1994

96. BARTOLOMEO MANFREDI
Carità romana
c. 1620
Oil on canvas; 130x97. Inv. 1890/10958

97. GHERARDO DELLE NOTTI
Adoration of the Child
1619-1620. Oil on canvas; 95.5x131
Inv. 1890/739. Restored: 1993

98. GHERARDO DELLE NOTTI
Supper with Lute Player
1619-1620. Oil on canvas; 144x212
Inv. 1890/730. Restored: 1993-1994

99. GHERARDO DELLE NOTTI
Wedding Supper
1613-1614. Oil on canvas; 138x203
Inv. 1890/735. Restored: 1994-1995

100. GHERARDO DELLE NOTTI
The Good Luck
1617-1619. Oil on canvas; 137x204
Inv. 1890/734. Restored: 1993-1994

101. FRANCESCO RUSTICI
Death of Lucretia
c. 1630
Oil on canvas; 175x259.5. Inv. 1890/6421

102. NICOLAS RÉGNIER
The Fortune Teller
c. 1635. Oil on canvas; 172x232
Inv. 1890 n. 9460. Restored: 1993

103. CARAVAGGESQUE PAINTER
Freeing of Peter from Prison
c. 1615-1620
Oil on canvas; 147x190
Inv. 1890 n. 578. Restored: 1993-1994

104. SPADARINO
Banquet of the Gods
c. 1625-1630. Oil on canvas; 124x193.5
Inv. 1890/2119. Restored: 1993

105. GUIDO RENI
David with the Head of Goliath
c. 1605. Oil on canvas; 222x147
Inv. 1890/3850. Restored: 1995

106. GUIDO RENI
*Madonna and Child
with Sts Lucia and Mary Magdalene*
c. 1625. Oil on canvas; 280x176
Inv. 1890/3088. Restored: 1995

107. GUIDO RENI
Saint Andrea Corsini
c.1629-1630. Oil on canvas; 233x155
Inv. 1890/10072 (purchased in 2000)

25

DIEGO VELÁZQUEZ
AND WORKSHOP
Philip IV of Spain on horseback

This portrait was in Madrid in 1651, owned by the Marquis Eliche. This great official portrait, typical of the Spanish court, probably derives from a similar subject painted by Rubens (c. 1628), known from a description, which was destroyed in Madrid in 1734. Whilst in the original the king was shown at the age of twenty-two, here the face is taken from a portrait by Velázquez (1645, now in the New York Frick Collection). The Florentine canvas reveals the hand of the Spanish painter in the face of the king, on the head of the horse, and in the masterly brushwork around the figures.

27

PIETER PAUL RUBENS
*Portrait
of Isabella Brandt*

"A very good companion [...] completely good, completely honest and beloved for her virtues": thus the great Flemish painter remembers his first wife, immediately after her death in 1626. Often portrayed by Rubens, Isabella is shown here half-length, shortly before her death, against a shady background of a curtain and a column. The portrait was given as a gift in 1705 by the Palatine Elector of the Rhine Johann Wilhelm to his brother-in-law Ferdinando de' Medici, who called it a "work of genius" from the "famous brush" of Rubens.

29

PIETER PAUL RUBENS
Triumph
(Triumphal entry
of Henri IV in Paris)

Like the *Battle*, this enormous canvas, now re-turned to the Uffizi after exemplary restoration, has an intriguing history. Both works, inspired by the life of Henri IV, formed part of a series left unfinished in 1630. At the death of Rubens in 1640 it was still in his studio at Antwerp. Maria de' Medici, widow of the King of France, had commissioned the Flemish artist, who may have been present at the royal wedding, celebrated by proxy in Florence in 1600, to paint a commemorative series of battles, sieges and triumphs of the King of France.

The series was to accompany the scenes from the life of the Queen, painted by Rubens from

1622 to 1625 for the Luxembourg Palace. Diplomatic and political problems (Maria was confined to Compiègne and then exiled) prevented the second project from being carried out, After the painter's death the canvases now in the Uffizi went to the collection of the Antwerp Canon Fréderic Lancelot, at Cam-

brai. Although the painter Charles Le Brun tried to buy them for the King of France, it was Apollonio Bassetti, secretary of Cosimo III, who managed to obtain them.
In 1687 they arrived from Antwerp at the port of Livorno, wound in great rolls, and from there to Florence.

56

REMBRANDT
Self-portrait as a Young man

Son of a rich miller from Leide, the artist left his native city in 1631 for Amsterdam. There he painted this self-portrait, which already displays confidence and acute psychological investigation. The painting may have been a gift from the Palatine Elector of the Rhine Johann Wilhelm (married to Anna Maria Luisa de' Medici) to the Florentine Gerini family. It was purchased by Ferdinand III of Lorraine in 1818. For Rembrandt self-portraiture was a lifelong concern, as if he wished to document every stage of his career, marked by at least eighty self-portraits.

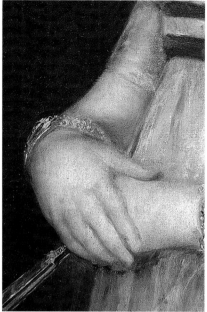

66

FRANCISCO GOYA Y LUCIENTES
Portrait of María Teresa,
Countess of Chinchón

Goya did portraits of María Teresa, daughter of his patron Luís de Borbón, from her childhood. In 1783 he also painted his patron's wife, María Teresa di Vallabriga, riding a horse (Uffizi, Inv. no. 9485). In 1797 María was to marry Manuel Godoy, the scheming minister of the King and favourite of the Queen.

For the Countess this was to be the start of an unhappy life, as can be guessed from this delicate portrait, in which the young girl's profile is repeated on the medallion bracelet around her wrist. Goya retained close ties of friendship with this woman, and he died like her in exile in France in 1828.

77

CANALETTO
View of the Ducal Palace in Venice

One of Canaletto's most often repeated views, this canvas, which once hung at Poggio Imperiale, has been linked to a drawing now at Windsor Castle (no. 7451). The painting shows the wharf and the Riva degli Schiavoni in limpid detail. For his perspective views Canaletto used a 'camera ottica': this box, a forerunner of the modern camera, contained mirrors which projected a view, through a series of reflections, onto a sheet so that the painter could copy it directly from life.

In the Uffizi canvas the foreground is dominated by gondolas and boats with figures busy rowing or throwing ropes. In the background can be seen the Zecca, the Old Library, the Ducal Palace and the Dandolo Palace. The painting can be dated with certainly before 1755, the year in which the Clock Tower underwent alterations which do not appear in it.

88

CARAVAGGIO
Sacrifice of Isaac

Caravaggio, inspired by the Biblical Book of Genesis, shows an angel stopping Abraham who in obedience to God is about to sacrifice his son Isaac. Beside the head of the boy, who is shouting desperately, is the ram sent by God to be sacrificed in his place. While in the Biblical text the angel speaks to Abraham from the sky, here he comes down to the ground to stay his hand directly.

The scene, painted with fine strokes of light against a serene landscape showing a Venetian influence, prefigures the sacrifice of Christ and symbolizes obedience and faith in accordance with the climate of renewed spirituality of the time. The chronology of this canvas is still doubtful: it was donated to the Uffizi by John F. Murray, son of the pre-Raphaelite painter. Its provenance is also uncertain, since it cannot be identified with certainty as the painting of an unknown subject for which Maffeo Barberini, who was later to become Pope Urban VIII, paid Caravaggio between 1603 and 1604.

The theme of the canvas in the Uffizi does, however, fit the description of a "sacrifice of Abraham who holds a knife to the throat of his son who shouts and falls down", painted for the Barberini family in 1672, according to the writer Giuseppe Bellori.

89

CARAVAGGIO
Medusa

Medusa with her head of snakes transformed anyone who looked at her into stone. "Run, for if amazement draws your eyes,/she will turn you into stone", wrote Gaspare Murtola in 1603, admiring the *Medusa* with her "poisonous hair/armed with a thousand snakes", painted in Rome by the "peintre maudit" for the Cardinal Del Monte as a gift to Ferdinando de' Medici. Astonishment is also expressed in the verses of Giovan Battista Marino (1614): "That fierce, harsh Gorgon,/to which they dedicate such horribly/viperish forms/her squalid pomp and frightful locks of hair". In 1631 the convex "rotella" (tournament shield) was on display at the Medicean Armoury, hanging on the arm of an Oriental suit of armour which was a gift from the Shah of Persia Abbas the Great to the Grand Duke.

91

CARAVAGGIO
The Adolescent Bacchus

Brought out of Depositi (store) in 1916, the now famous Bacchus was attributed to Caravaggio by Roberto Longhi. In all probability the canvas dates from the time when the young artist from Lombardy was working in Rome for Cardinal Francesco Maria Del Monte (c. 1595-1600), a man of culture, who may have ordered the painting as a gift for Ferdinando de' Medici, as he did with the *Medusa*. It has been suggested that the face of the young god of wine is a portrait of the Sicilian painter Mario Monnitti, who lived with Caravaggio in Rome for some time. The Dionysian myth, here loaded with philosophical and religious symbols, is portrayed with sensuality and crude realism: the reddened cheeks, the moist lips, the dirty fingernails and the worm-eaten, half-rotten fruit.

107

GUIDO RENI
Saint Andrea Corsini

Up to now the Uffizi had four canvases by the great Bolognese painter, among them the *David with the Head of Goliath*, shown here. In 2000 the Gallery acquired the refined canvas depicting *Saint Andrea Corsini*. The work, distinguished by a brilliant color scheme, shows the Florentine saint to whom the Corsini family dedicated a magnificent chapel in the church of Santa Maria del Carmine in the 17ᵗʰ century. Born in 1301, Bishop of Fiesole in 1349, accredited with several miracles, in 1368 Andrea Corsini was sent by Pope Urban V to carry out an important diplomatic mission, to keep Bologna from falling into the hands of the Visconti. Guido Reni has shown the saint in devout prayer, attended by cherubim.

Room 42 ❖ Niobe

The Niobe Room (opposite page) has been restored and rearranged after the severe damage caused by the 1993 bombing. This room was planned by Pietro Leopoldo to display a group of classical sculptures (Roman copies of late Hellenistic originals). Found in the 16th century in a vineyard in Rome near the Lateran, they recall the myth of Niobe, destroyed with her children by Apollo and Diana. This sensational discovery was announced in a letter of 1583 written by the sculptor and restorer Valerio Cioli to the secretary of the Grand Duke Francesco I. After several months the statues were acquired by the Grand Duke's brother, Ferdinando, then Cardinal in Rome, who restored them and took them to the Villa Medici. Five years later he sent casts of the sculptures to Florence, which were displayed in the Gallery until Pietro Leopoldo, as mentioned, brought them to Tuscany in 1770. The restoration of the first group (more pieces arrived later) was entrusted to Innocenzo Spinazzi and completed in 1776; by 1795 the statues were on display in the Neoclassical room, designed by Gaspare Paoletti and decorated with light-colored stuccoes and gilded reliefs.

The works

JUSTUS SUSTERMANS
The Florentine Senate Swears Allegiance to Ferdinando II de' Medici
1621
Oil on canvas; 397x626
Inv. 1890 no. 721
Restored: 2002

Niobian climbing a rock
Pentelic marble
Height 150
Inv. 1914 no. 306

Psyche in torment
(previously thought to be a *Niobian*, head not pertinent)
Pentelic marble and Lunense
Height 125
Inv. 1914 no. 305

Running Niobian
Pentelic marble
Height 152
Inv. 1914 no. 304

Muse
(previously thought to be a *Niobian*, head not pertinent)
Pentelic marble
Height 153
Inv. 1914 no. 303

Niobe's Eldest son
Pentelic marble
Height 170
Inv. 1914 no. 502

Tutor of Niobe's children
(not pertinent to the group)
Pentelic marble
Height 181
Inv. 1914 no. 501

Running Niobian
Greek marble
Height 176
Inv. 1914 no. 300

Niobian (?)
the so-called Narcissus
(modern head)
Pentelic marble
Height 110
Inv. 1914 no. 299

Dying Niobian
Greek marble
Length 185
Inv. 1914 no. 298
Restored: 1994

Muse
Pentelic marble
Height 186.5
Inv. 1914 no. 29

Selene (?)
(previously thought to be *The Niobians' nurse*, head not pertinent)
Pentelic marble
Height 189
Inv. 1914 no. 296

Niobe with her Youngest daughter
Pentelic marble
Height 228
Inv. 1914 no. 294

Niobe's Eldest daughter
Pentelic marble
Height 181
Inv. 1914 no. 293

Niobe's Youngest son
Pentelic marble
Height 130
Inv. 1914 no. 292

Running Niobian
(head not pertinent)
Pentelic marble
Height 138
Inv. 1914 no. 291

Falling Niobian
Pentelic and Italic marble
Height 129
Inv. 1914 no. 290

Falling Niobian
Pentelic marble
Height 124
Inv. 1914 no. 289

Horse
(from Magliana)
Roman art,
1st century BC
Pentelic marble
Height 270
Inv. 1914 no. 69

Running Niobian

Found, like the other sculptures exhibited here, in 1583 at Vigna Tommasini near the Lateran, this statue represents one of Niobe's seven children attempting to flee from Apollo's arrows. According to the myth Niobe, daughter of Tantalus and wife of Anphione, was the mother of 7 boys and 7 girls whom Latona, out of jealousy, caused to be slain by Apollo and Diana. The mother was transformed into a rocky cliff.

Vasari Corridor

The most spectacular and famous corridor of the world was created in 1565. Giorgio Vasari, the architect of the court, had already been enlarging and restructuring the new Medici residence at Palazzo Vecchio for some time, bringing to an end the great Uffizi project. During the preparations for the magnificent royal wedding of Francesco de' Medici and Jean of Austria, the architect was commissioned by Cosimo I to complete in record time, from March to September 1565, a corridor that was to lead from the Uffizi to Palazzo Pitti, which had been bought in 1549 by Eleonora di Toledo, wife of Cosimo. The Vasari Corridor starts from the West wing of the Uffizi, follows the Arno in an astonishing raised path that passes over the shops of the left parapet of the Ponte Vecchio, overlooks the interior of the church of Santa Felicita, (then the Palatine Chapel), and finally reaches the Boboli Gardens, where works had been going on for some time under the direction of many architects and sculptors. An extraordinary and highly symbolic urban intervention in the ducal city, the Corridor, almost a kilometre long with unique views from its windows and circular apertures, was designed as an exclusive walkway for the Duke, the Princes, and high dignitaries of the court. It was only opened for public use in 1866 when Florence was capital of the Republic. It was then that its real history as a museum began, interrupted for long periods by the damage caused by World War II, the flood (1966), and the bomb (1993). Now restored, the Corridor contains around 800 paintings; on the staircase and in first stretch there are important works from the 17th and 18th century, while on the Ponte Vecchio the most famous collection of self-portraits in the world is displayed, which was begun by Cardinal Leopoldo and is still growing.

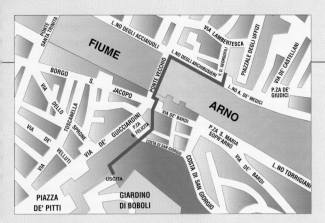

Elisabeth Vigée-Le Brun
Self-portrait

1790
Oil on canvas; 100x81
Inv. 1890 no. 1905

In the golden twilight of the Paris Ancien Régime, this rich and fashionable artist, the only woman with an academic title, left France at the outbreak of the revolution. Official painter to Marie Antoinette, she portrayed herself painting a portrait of her queen, in this work which had been commissioned by Pietro Leopoldo in Rome: thus creating a self-portrait with a portrait, immediately praised and copied.

Sir Joshua Reynolds
Self-portrait

Signed and dated 1775
Oil on canvas; 71,5x58
Inv. 1890 no. 1932. Restored: 1995

Appointed 'Doctor of Civil Law' at the University of Oxford in 1773, Reynolds portrayed himself in this guise that same year, in an oval portrait now in a private collection. A year later he portrayed himself in a similar pose and wearing the same mantle, in another self-portrait painted expressly for the Uffizi. In this canvas, which was immediately copied, he holds a scroll with drawings by 'the divine Michelangelo'.

Eugène Delacroix
Self-portrait

c. 1840
Oil on canvas; 66x54
Inv. 1890 no. 3914

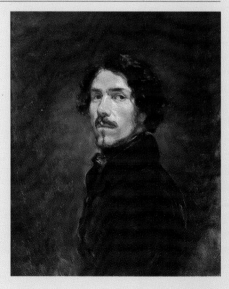

The artist must build "a mysterious bridge between the soul of the characters and the spectators", wrote Eugène Delacroix in his diary.
This concept is confirmed by his self-portrait – transferred to the Uffizi Gallery in 1912 – stylistically close to another conserved at the Louvre and to the intense *Portrait of Chopin* from 1938 (also at the Louvre Museum).

Contini Bonacossi Collection

The Contini Bonacossi Collection, among the most important of this century, was acquired as a donation by the State in 1969. In addition to ceramics, furniture and extraordinary sculptures such as Bernini's St. Laurence, *it contains works by Italian and foreign artists ranging from the 13th to the 18th century with masterpieces such as Sassetta's* Madonna of the Snow. *Among the great artists whose works could not be represented here for lack of space are Paolo Veneziano, Giovanni Bellini, Giuseppe Maria Crespi, Goya, Velásquez, and Zurbarán. The collection, exhibited since 1974 in Palazzo Pitti, has now found a more appropriate home amongst the Uffizi displays, in specially restored 14th century rooms used in granducal times as a residence for footmen.*

The works

Room 1

1. FLORENTINE SCHOOL
*Bust of Ludovico
da Verrazzano*
mid-17th century
White marble
Height 78; base 11
Contini Bonacossi Inv. no. 46

Room 2

2. DUCCIO DI BONINSEGNA (ATTR.)
Madonna and Child
First decades of 14th century
Tempera on wood
84x55
Contini Bonacossi Inv. no. 26

3. GIOVANNI DEL BIONDO
*St. John the Baptist
and eleven episodes from his life*
Second half of the 14th century
Tempera on wood
275x180
Contini Bonacossi Inv. no. 27

4. AGNOLO GADDI
*Madonna and Child
with Sts. Benedict, John
the Evangelist and Miniato*
c. 1375-1380
Tempera on wood
222x300
Contini Bonacossi Inv. no. 29

**5. UGOLINO DI NERIO
KNOW AS UGOLINO DA SIENA**
*Madonna and Child
with Sts. Peter and Paul*
First half of the 14th century
Tempera on wood
150x58 (central panel)
126x44 (side panels)
Contini Bonacossi Inv. no. 4

6. DOMENICO DI NICCOLÒ "DEI CORI"
Announcing Angel
Third decade of the 15th century
Polychrome wood
Height 166
Contini Bonacossi Inv. no. 43

7. SASSETTA
*Madonna of the Snow
Altarpiece*
c. 1430-1432
Tempera on wood
240x256
Contini Bonacossi Inv. no. 1
Restored: 1998

8. DOMENICO DI NICCOLÒ "DEI CORI"
Our Lady of the Annunciation
Third decade of the 15th century
Polychrome wood, height 166
Contini Bonacossi Inv. no. 44

9. FLORENTINE SCHOOL
Madonna and Child with two Saints
c. 1315
Tempera on wood
103x176
Contini Bonacossi Inv. no. 31

10. CIMABUE (ATTR.)
*Madonna and Child enthroned,
two Angels, Sts. Francis and Dominic*
Late 13th-early 14th century
Tempera on wood
133x82
Contini Bonacossi Inv. no. 32

Room 3

11. GIOVANNI DI FRANCESCO
*Madonna with Child enthroned
and two Angels' heads*
c. 1450
Tempera on wood
105x59
Contini Bonacossi Inv. no. 5

12. ANDREA DEL CASTAGNO
The Pazzi Family Madonna
c. 1443
Detached fresco
290x212
Contini Bonacossi Inv. no. 2

**13. GIOVANNI BELLINI
KNOW AS GIAMBELLINO**
St. Jerome in the desert
c. 1479
Oil on wood
151x113
Contini Bonacossi Inv. no. 25

14. CIMA DA CONEGLIANO
St. Jerome in the desert
c. 1505
Oil on wood
33x27.5
Contini Bonacossi Inv. no. 19

15. VINCENZO CATENA
The Supper at Emmaus
c. 1520-1530
Oil on canvas
130x241
Contini Bonacossi Inv. no. 15

16. FLORENTINE SCHOOL
Della Robbian Tondo with coat-of-arms of the Aldobrandini Family
Late 15th-early 16th century
Glazed terracotta, diam. 85
Contini Bonacossi Inv. no. 90

17. FLORENTINE SCHOOL
Della Robbian Tondo with coat-of-arms of the Altoviti Family
16th century
Glazed terracotta
w. m.
Contini Bonacossi Inv. no. 87

18. PAOLO VENEZIANO
Nativity of St. Nicholas
c. 1346
Tempera on wood
74.5x54.5
Contini Bonacossi Inv. no. 6

19. PAOLO VENEZIANO
Charity of St. Nicholas
c. 1346
Tempera on wood
73x53
Contini Bonacossi Inv. no. 7

Room 4

20. FRANCIA
St. Francis
c. 1490
Tempera on wood
65x44
Contini Bonacossi Inv. no. 30

21. GIOVAN ANTONIO BOLTRAFFIO
Portrait of the poet Casio
c. 1490-1500
Oil on wood
51.5x37
Contini Bonacossi Inv. no. 28

22. DEFENDENTE FERRARI
Madonna nursing the Holy Child
1520-1530
Oil on wood
75x48.5
Contini Bonacossi Inv. no. 8

23. GIOVAN GEROLAMO SAVOLDO
The Magdalene
Variously dated c. 1521 or 1533
Oil on canvas
85x79
Contini Bonacossi Inv. no. 17

24. FRANCESCO MORONE (ATTR.)
Announcing Angel
Early 16ᵗʰ century
Oil on canvas
208x94
Contini Bonacossi Inv. no. 12

25. FRANCESCO MORONE (ATTR.)
Our Lady of the Annunciation
Early 16ᵗʰ century
Oil on canvas
208x94
Contini Bonacossi Inv. no. 11

Room 5

26. AGOSTINO BUSTI KNOW AS BAMBAJA
St. Francis
Early 16ᵗʰ century
White marble
59.5x21
Contini Bonacossi Inv. no. 40

27. AGOSTINO BUSTI KNOW AS BAMBAJA
Fame
Early 16ᵗʰ century
White marble
54x22.5
Contini Bonacossi Inv. no. 39

28. AGOSTINO BUSTI KNOW AS BAMBAJA
Saint Catherine of Alexandria
Early 16ᵗʰ century
White marble
59.5x23
Contini Bonacossi Inv. no. 41

29. BRAMANTINO
Madonna and Child with eight Saints
First decades of the 17ᵗʰ century
Tempera on wood
203x167
Contini Bonacossi Inv. no. 3

30. BOCCACCIO BOCCACCINO
St. John the Evangelist
c. 1510
Oil on wood
75x58
Contini Bonacossi Inv. no. 14

31. BOCCACCIO BOCCACCINO
St. Matthew (?)
c. 1510
Oil on wood
76x59
Contini Bonacossi Inv. no. 13

32. LOMBARD SCHOOL
Evangelist
Late 15ᵗʰ century
Marble
Height 86
Contini Bonacossi Inv. no. 42

33. BERNARDINO ZENALE
The Archangel St. Michael
Late 15ᵗʰ century
Oil on wood
115x51
Contini Bonacossi Inv. no. 10

34. BERNARDINO ZENALE
St. Bernard and a Cistercian monk
Late 15ᵗʰ century
Oil on wood
113x50
Contini Bonacossi Inv. no. 9

35. LOMBARD SCHOOL (PREVIOUSLY ATTR. TO GIOVANNI ANTONIO AMADEO)
Flagellation of Christ
Late 15ᵗʰ century
White marble
70x49
Contini Bonacossi Inv. no. 38

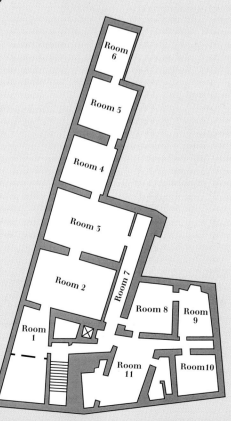

Room 6

36. GIUSEPPE MARIA CRESPI KNOW AS SPAGNOLO
The Scullery-Maid
First half of the 18ᵗʰ century
Oil on canvas
57x43
Contini Bonacossi Inv. no. 20

37. PAOLO VERONESE
Portrait of Iseppo da Porto with his son Adrian
c. 1551
Oil on canvas
247x137
Contini Bonacossi Inv. no. 16

38. JACOPO BASSANO
Madonna and Child with the infant St. John
Oil on canvas
79x60
Contini Bonacossi Inv. no. 18

39. GIAN LORENZO BERNINI
The martyred St. Lawrence
c. 1613-1617
White marble
70x112x45
Contini Bonacossi Inv. no. 36

40. JACOPO TINTORETTO
Portrait of a Gentlemen in furs
c. 1553
Oil on canvas
110x91.5
Contini Bonacossi Inv. no. 33

Room 10

41. FRANCISCO DE ZURBARÁN
St. Anthony Abbot
c. 1640
Oil on canvas
177x117
Contini Bonacossi Inv. no. 23

42. EL GRECO (ATTR., OR FOLLOWER)
The tears of St. Peter
Late 16ᵗʰ century (or 17ᵗʰ century)
Oil on canvas
175x126
Contini Bonacossi Inv. no. 21

43. FRANCISCO GOYA Y LUCIENTES
Portrait of a Bullfighter
c. 1797-1800
Oil on canvas
53x42
Contini Bonacossi Inv. no. 22

44. DIEGO VELÁZQUEZ
The water Vender of Seville
c. 1620
Oil on canvas, 104x75
Contini Bonacossi Inv. no. 24

Room 11

45. JACOPO TINTORETTO
Athena and Arachne
c. 1597
Oil on canvas, 145x272
Contini Bonacossi Inv. no. 35

46. PIETRO BRACCI
Portrait bust of Pope Benedict XIII
c. 1724-1730
Bronze, 92x73
Contini Bonacossi Inv. no. 37

47. JACOPO TINTORETTO
Diana and Endymion
c. 1597
Oil on canvas, 145x272
Contini Bonacossi Inv. no. 34

SASSETTA
Madonna of the Snow Altarpiece

This beautiful altarpiece, whose side panels have been lost, was painted for the San Bonifacio chapel in the Siena Cathedral. It is among the most interesting works of this painter from Cortona, endowed with extraordinary creative phantasy, who worked mainly in Siena. The title alludes to the miraculous snowfall which took place on the Esquiline in Rome on August 5th 358, a day which was then consecrated to Saint Mary of the Snow. The miracle, preannounced by the Madonna to the patrician Giovanni, is said to have determined the place where the prestigious basilica of Santa Maria Maggiore was to be built, financed by the patrician. In the predella, composed of seven small scenes, are the events which led to the foundation of the Basilica by Pope Liberius. The simplicity of the portrayal, close to the frescoes of Masaccio and Masolino in the Carmine, is united with what has been defined as "the most radical experiment in realistic painting" of that time.

12

ANDREA DEL CASTAGNO
The Pazzi Family Madonna

This large fresco comes from the chapel of the Trebbio Castle near Pontassieve. In 1427 the castle belonged to Andrea dei Pazzi, who had commissioned to Brunelleschi to build the Pazzi chapel in Santa Croce.

Against a surprising background, with two angels descending head down to hold up a precious tapestry, the Madonna and Child are flanked by St. John the Baptist and St. Jerome. The children portrayed at the far left and right of the painting are, according to a likely hypothesis, the twins Niccolò and Oretta, grandchildren of Andrea Pazzi, who were born in 1437.

On the basis of their presumed age the fresco can be dated at about 1443, immediately after the Tuscan artist's return from Venice. It is probable that the tondo at the top of the painting originally coincided with a window or a coat-of-arms in the Trebbio chapel.

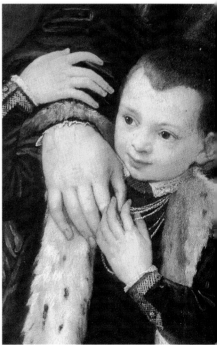

37

PAOLO VERONESE
Portrait of Iseppo da Porto
with his son Adrian

Together with this portrait of himself with his son, Count Iseppo da Porto, a nobleman of Vicenza, commissioned Veronese to paint a similar portrait of his wife Livia Thiene with their daughter Porzia (now in Baltimore, Walters Art Gallery). In the Uffizi painting the father and son, framed by a doorway, are caught in a moment of affectionate embrace. The child's small hand is intertwined with the large hand of the Count, who for this reason has taken off his glove. Veronese also decorated for him the palace in Vicenza designed by Palladio and completed in 1552.

42

EL GRECO
(ATTR., OR FOLLOWER)
The tears of St. Peter

The iconography of St. Peter weeping after having denied Christ three times was a theme inspired by the Counter-Reformation. El Greco was, it seems, the first artist to deal with this subject, and with success, to judge by the sixteen variations, many of them workshop production, painted about thirty years. This work conserved in the Uffizi, where the Angel of the Resurrection and the Magdalene appear beyond the grotto, is among those deemed non-authentic by the most studies. It could have been painted much later than its prototype, perhaps already in the 18th century.

Index

Essential Bibliography

G. VASARI, *The Lives of the Most Eminent Painters, Sculptors and Architects*, 10 vols., London 1912-1915.
R. OFFNER, *A Critical and Historical Corpus of Florentine Painting*, continued under the direction of M. Boskovits and M. Gregori, Giunti, Florence 1984-1999.
G. FOSSI, *The Uffizi. The Official Guide*, Firenze Musei-Giunti, Florence 1998, second revised edition 2002.
The New exit for the Uffizi. Aulenti, Botta, Foster, Gregotti, Hollein, Isozaki, edited by A. Godoli, Firenze Musei-Giunti, Florence 1998; G. FOSSI, *Uffizi Gallery. Art, History, Collec-*

tions, Firenze Musei-Giunti, Florence 2002[2]; G. DI PASQUALE-F. PAOLUCCI, *The Ancient Sculptures of the Uffizi*, Firenze Musei-Giunti, Florence 2001.
For updated information on some of the masterpieces:
D. CORSINI, *Botticelli. "The birth of Venus"*; G. FOSSI, *Sandro Botticelli, "Primavera"*; EAD., *Giotto, "The Ognissanti Madonna"*; EAD., *Michelangelo, "Doni Tondo"*: all edited by Firenze Musei-Giunti, Florence 1998; C. ACIDINI, *Grotesques. The Painted Ceilings at the Uffizi Gallery*, Firenze Musei-Giunti, Florence 1999.

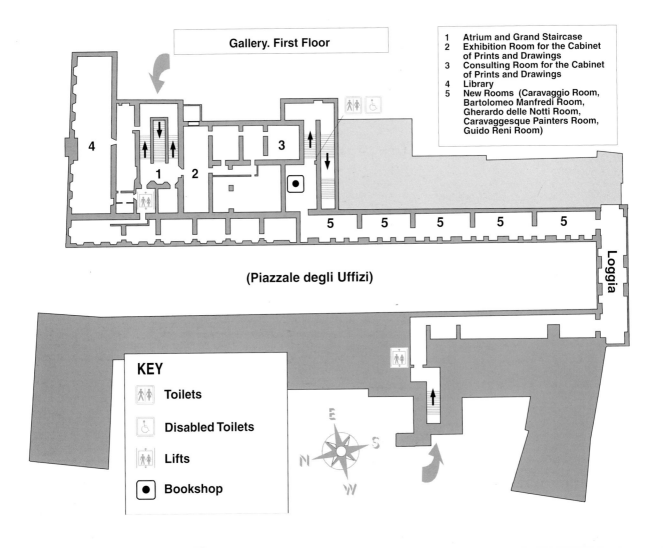

Gallery. First Floor

1 Atrium and Grand Staircase
2 Exhibition Room for the Cabinet of Prints and Drawings
3 Consulting Room for the Cabinet of Prints and Drawings
4 Library
5 New Rooms (Caravaggio Room, Bartolomeo Manfredi Room, Gherardo delle Notti Room, Caravaggesque Painters Room, Guido Reni Room)

(Piazzale degli Uffizi)

Loggia

KEY

Toilets

Disabled Toilets

Lifts

Bookshop

as   ap   ar

ac   ha   ta

①

apple   apple

tasty   tasty

share   share

snack   snack

a tasty apple

a tasty apple

Ages 8+

Trace with Me

Cursive Letters

six xylophone notes

six xylophone notes

Beth Burn

Beth Burn

Thinking Kids®
Carson-Dellosa Publishing LLC
Greensboro, North Carolina

Make learning how to write in cursive a fun and successful experience. Each tear-out page in this book is a lesson that teaches you how to write a lowercase or uppercase cursive letter. Each lesson includes:

- A model letter with numbered arrows that show how to form the letter, step by step.
- Letters, letter combinations, and words to trace for cursive writing practice.

In cursive writing, all lowercase letters connect to the letter that follows. Some uppercase letters join the next letter, and some do not. Follow this guide:

These uppercase letters join the next letter.	These uppercase letters do not join the next letter.
a, C, E, H, J, K, m, n, R, U, Y, Z	*B, D, F, G, I, L, O, P, Q, S, T, V, W, X*

Thinking Kids®
Carson-Dellosa Publishing LLC
PO Box 35665
Greensboro, NC 27425 USA

Printed in the USA • All rights reserved.
03-140197784

ISBN 978-1-4838-5196-9

Alex was eight in April.

Alex was eight in April.

Al   Ap   Ac

As   Am   Ag

Alex   Alex

April   April

Alaska

Alabama

black bats
black bats

ba   bt   bb

by   br   ib

bats   bats

black   black

brown

nibble

Beth Burns blows bubbles.

Beth Burns blows bubbles.

Beth Beth

Burns

Boise Boise

Boston

Bolivia

Beijing

a cute cat

a cute cat

ca   cu   co

ic   rc   scr

cat   cat   cat

cute cute cute

calico   calico

colorful

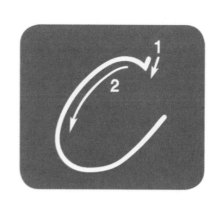

Casey cheers for the Comets.

Casey cheers for the Comets.

Ca   Co   Cy

Ce   Ch   Cl

Casey

Comets

Colorado

Canada

good dog
good dog

do   da   dr

od   nd   dd

dog   dog   dog

good   good

friend

cuddle

Dr. Davis will help.

Dr. Davis will help.

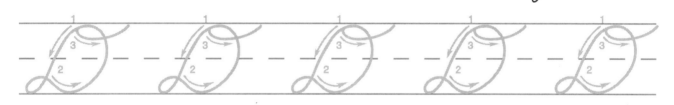

Dr. Davis

David

Delaware

December

Denmark

Dallas

eleven eggs

eleven eggs

eg   el   en

le   ve   ze

eggs   eggs

white white

dozen dozen

eleven

Ellis Edwards is ten.

Ellis Edwards is ten.

El   Ed   Ea

Ec   Ep   Eu

Ellis   Ellis

Edwards

Earth   Earth

Ecuador

a furry fox

a furry fox

fo   fa   fu

fy   ff   ife

fox   fox   fox

fast   fast

furry

forest

Follow me to Fay's Farm.

Follow me to Fay's Farm.

Fay   Fay

Fay's Farm

Friday

Florida

February

Finland

a hungry goat

a hungry goat

go gr gu

gi ag ng

goat goat

gobble gobble

hungry

greedy

Grandma gave Gabe a gift.

Grandma gave Gabe a gift.

Gabe Gabe

Gail Gail

German

Grandma

Great Lakes

Georgia

birthday hat

birthday hat

h h h h h h

h h h h h h

h h h h h h

ha ho hd

ch sh th

hat hat

happy

birthday

hooray

Hana loves Halloween.

Hana loves Halloween.

Ha   Ho   Hy

He   Hi   Hu

Hana   Hana

Halloween

Houston

Honolulu

an icy igloo

an icy igloo

ic ig id

it id ing

icy icy icy

igloo igloo

snowing

outside

Inez lives in Iowa.

Inez lives in Iowa.

Inez   Inez

Iowa   Iowa

Idaho

Indiana

Iceland

Ireland

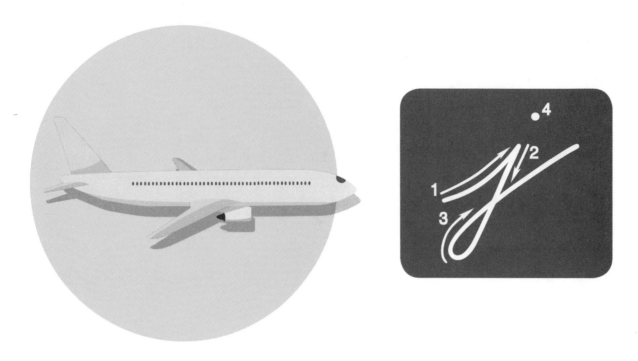

a jumbo jet

a jumbo jet

je   jo   ju

ja   ji   nj

jet   jet   jet

jostle   jostle

enjoy   enjoy

jumbo

Josh jogs in January.

Josh jogs in January.

Jo   Ja   Ju

Ji   Je   Jy

Josh   Josh

January

Jackson

Japan

pink kites

pink kites

ki ky ke

sk nk rk

pink pink

sky sky

kites kites

park park

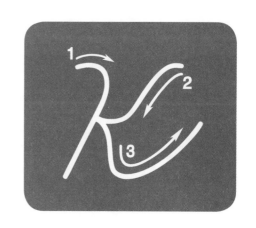

King Kyle will talk.

King Kyle will talk.

Ki Ky Ka

Kw Ke Ko

King Kyle

Kansas

Kentucky

Korean

a male lion

a male lion

le   li   la

at   et   ll

mate   mate

lion   lion

jungle

animal

Look for Lilac Lane.

Look for Lilac Lane.

Lincoln

Louisiana

Labor Day

Lake Lanier

Lilac Lane

Los Angeles

my milk

my milk

mi my mm

mu om rm

my my my

milk milk

yummy

mustache

Mr. Mesa teaches math.

Mr. Mesa teaches math.

Mr   Me   Mo

Ma   Mi   My

Monday

Mr. Mesa

Mars Mars

Mississippi

a nice nest

a nice nest

ne ni nt

nn in ing

nest nest

nice nice

wing wing

robin robin

Nikki knows Neptune.

Nikki knows Neptune.

Ni   Ne   No

Na   Nu   Ny

Nikki Nikki

Neptune

Nebraska

November

a strong ox
a strong ox

oy   on   ov

ro   wo   oo

ox   ox   ox

work   work

horn   horn

strong

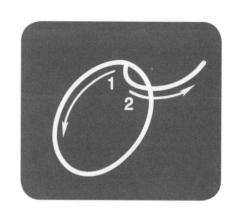

Omar celebrates October.

Omar celebrates October.

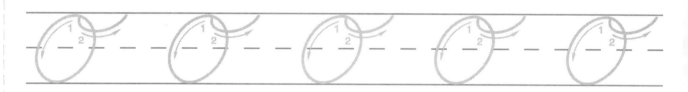

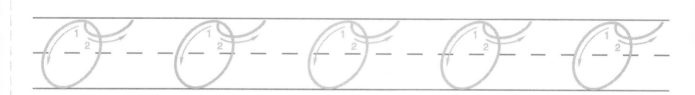

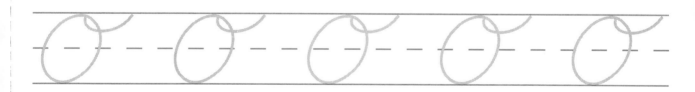

Omar Omar

October

Ohio Ohio

Oklahoma

Ozarks

Arctic Ocean

pancakes on a plate

pancakes on a plate

pt   pa   pr

pi   up   sp

plate   plate

syrup syrup

pile   pile

pancakes

Pete passed Pat's Pets.

Pete passed Pat's Pets.

Pete   Pete

Pat's Pets

Pluto Pluto

Peoria

Poland

Pacific Ocean

questions on a quiz

questions on a quiz

qu   qu   qu

eq   aq   sq

quiz   quiz

equal equal

questions

required

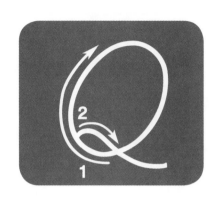

Queen Quinn wears aqua.

Queen Quinn wears aqua.

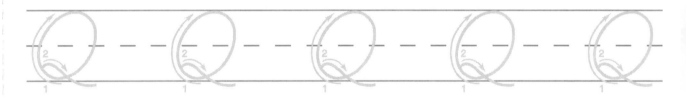

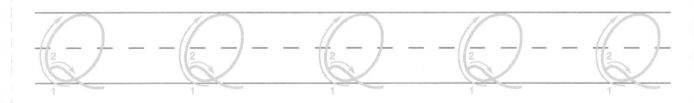

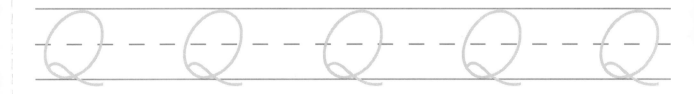

Quebec

Quentin

Quito Quito

Quincy

Queen

Quinn

spring rain
spring rain

ra   ri   rm

or   pr   wr

rain   rain

storm

spring

sprinkle

Ride down River Road.

Ride down River Road.

Ro   Ri   Rh

Ra   Ru   Ry

Roosevelt

River Road

Rio Grande

Russia

summer sunshine

summer sunshine

sh   su   st

sa   rs   ns

shore   shore

sand   sand

summer

sunshine

Stop at the sign.

Stop at the sign.

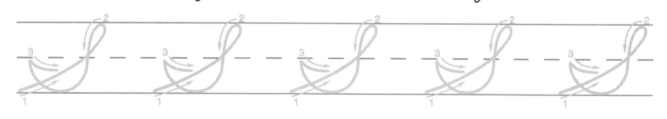

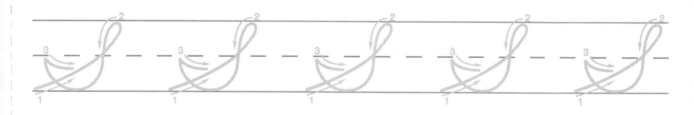

Saturn

Saturday

Sunday

September

Scotland

Stop! Stop!

a striped tiger

a striped tiger

ta   ti   tr

th   st   it

cat   cat   cat

tail   tail

tiger   tiger

striped

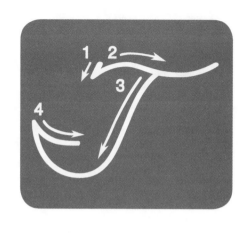

Tish trumpets on Tuesday.

Tish trumpets on Tuesday.

Fish

Tuesday

Thursday

Toronto

Tennessee

Texas Texas

a purple umbrella

a purple umbrella

ur um ut

un ou pu

up up up

pour pour

purple

umbrella

Uncle Upton visited us.

Uncle Upton visited us.

Ut — Un — Up

Ug — Ur — Uk

Utah — Utah

U.S.A.

Ukraine

Uncle Upton

a van to drive

a van to drive

va   ve   vy

av   iv   ev

van   van

drive   drive

wave   wave

travel

Vi likes Valentine's Day.

Vi likes Valentine's Day.

Venus Venus

Vermont

Virginia

Vi Vi Vi

Valentine's

Day

wheels on a wagon

wheels on a wagon

wa wh we

wi sw aw

walk walk

away away

wagon

wheels

Walk when it is safe.

Walk when it is safe.

Walla Walla

Wednesday

Washington

Walt Disney

Wisconsin

Walk now.

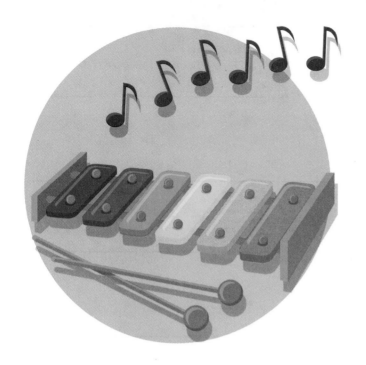

six xylophone notes

six xylophone notes

xt *xy* *xi*

ox *ix* *ex*

six six six

next next

expert

xylophone

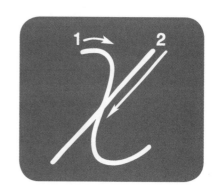

X-ray Xavier next.

X-ray Xavier next.

Xi'an Xi'an

Xenia Xenia

X-ray

Xavier

Xander

Xinjiang

yellow yarn

yellow yarn

ye   ya   yo

zy   ay   ty

yarn   yarn

fray   fray

yellow

fuzzy

Yvette Yates yo-yos.

Yvette Yates yo-yos.

Ya   Yu   Yo

Ye   Yi   Yv

Yvette

Yates   Yates

Yukon Yukon

Youngstown

a grazing zebra

a grazing zebra

ze   zo   zi

ez   zy   az

zebra   zebra

zoom   zoom

breeze

grazing

Zoe Zimmer won a prize.

Zoe Zimmer won a prize.

Zo   Zi   Ze

Za   Zu   Zy

Zoe   Zoe   Zoe

Zimmer

Zurich

New Zealand

$\mathcal{A}a$ $\mathcal{A}a$ $\mathcal{A}a$

$\mathcal{B}b$ $\mathcal{B}b$ $\mathcal{B}b$

$\mathcal{C}c$ $\mathcal{C}c$ $\mathcal{C}c$

$\mathcal{D}d$ $\mathcal{D}d$ $\mathcal{D}d$

Ee   Ee   Ee

Ff   Ff   Ff

Gg   Gg   Gg

Hh   Hh   Hh

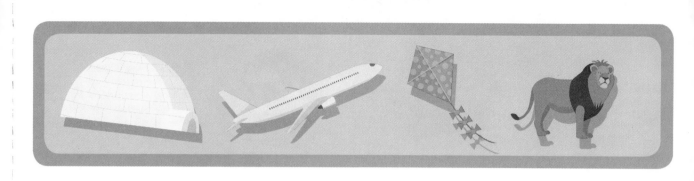

Ii Ii Ii

Jj Jj Jj

Kk Kk Kk

Ll Ll Ll

$\mathcal{N}\,m\ \mathcal{N}\,m$

$\mathcal{N}\,m\ \mathcal{N}\,m\ \mathcal{N}\,m$

$\mathcal{O}\,o\ \mathcal{O}\,o\ \mathcal{O}\,o$

$\mathcal{P}\,p\ \mathcal{P}\,p\ \mathcal{P}\,p$

$Qq \quad Qq \quad Qq$

$Rr \quad Rr \quad Rr$

$Ss \quad Ss \quad Ss$

$Tt \quad Tt \quad Tt$

Uu Uu Uu

Vv Vv Vv

Ww Ww Ww

Xx   Xx Xx   Xx Xx

Yy   Yy Yy   Yy Yy

Zz   Zz Zz   Zz Zz

Write the missing uppercase or lowercase letter.

_g_

_S_

_B_

_f_

_l_

_P_

_n_

_Z_

_m_

_w_

Cut out the flash cards on pages 115-127. Use your finger to trace the letters on each card.

Page is blank for cutting activity on previous page.

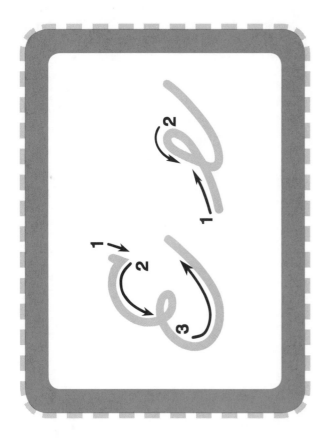

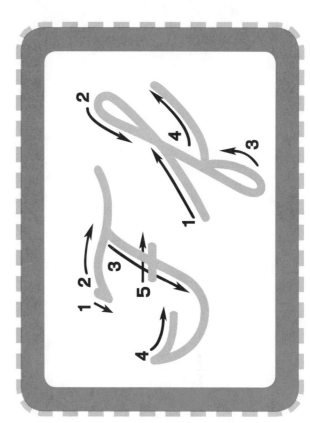

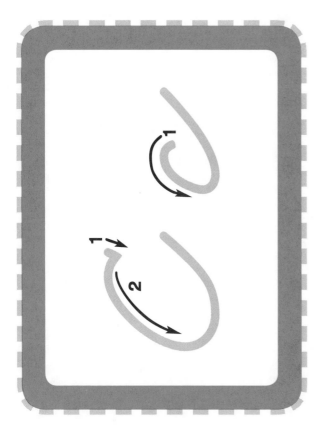

Page is blank for cutting activity on previous page.

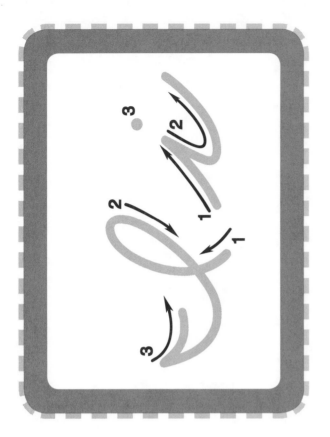

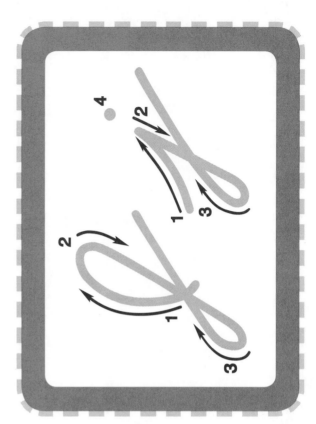

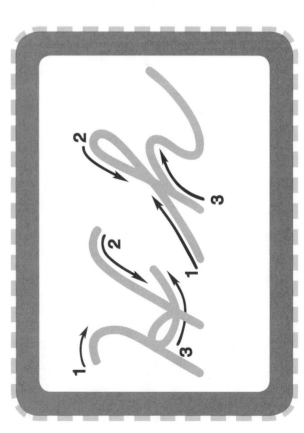

Page is blank for cutting activity on previous page.

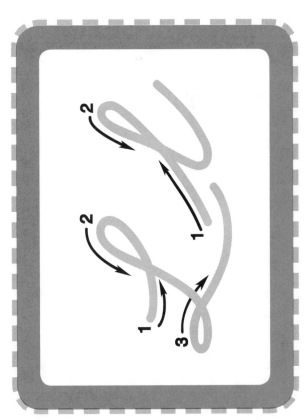

Page is blank for cutting activity on previous page.

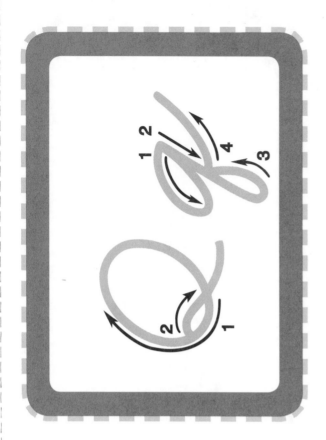

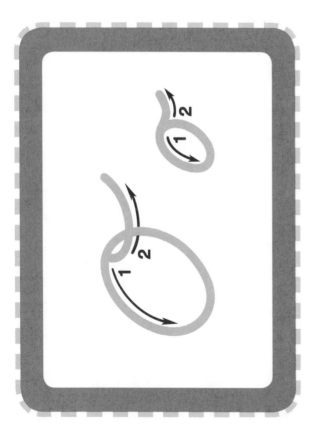

Page is blank for cutting activity on previous page.

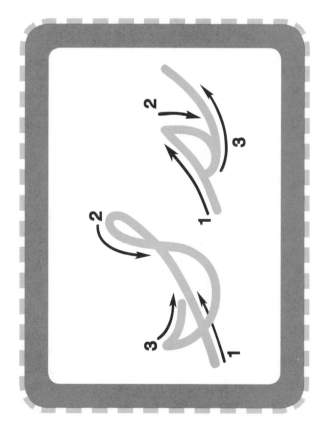

Page is blank for cutting activity on previous page.